SpringBoard®

English Language Development

California Edition

Grade 6

 CollegeBoard

ABOUT THE COLLEGE BOARD

The College Board is a mission-driven not-for-profit organization that connects students to college success and opportunity. Founded in 1900, the College Board was created to expand access to higher education. Today, the membership association is made up of more than 6,000 of the world's leading educational institutions and is dedicated to promoting excellence and equity in education. Each year, the College Board helps more than seven million students prepare for a successful transition to college through programs and services in college readiness and college success—including the SAT® and the Advanced Placement Program®. The organization also serves the education community through research and advocacy on behalf of students, educators and schools. For further information, visit www.collegeboard.com.

ISBN: 978-1-4573-0476-7
ISBN: 1-4573-0476-7

2 3 4 5 6 7 8   19 20 21 22
Printed in the United States of America

ACKNOWLEDGMENTS

The College Board gratefully acknowledges the outstanding work of the classroom teachers, reviewers, and writers who have been integral to the development of this program. The end product is testimony to their expertise, understanding of student learning needs, and dedication to rigorous English language arts instruction that is accessible to all students.

Patty M. Blome
English Language Arts teacher
Mar Vista Academy
San Diego, California

Shinay Bowman
English Language Arts Coach
King Middle School
San Bernardino, California

Michelle Callahan-Dumont
English Teacher
Sunnyside High School
Tucson, Arizona

Michael Gudex
English Language Arts Teacher
Sun Valley Magnet School
Sun Valley, California

Maria Larios-Horton
Director of Multilingual and Migrant
Education Programs
Santa Maria Joint Union High School
District
Santa Maria, California

Eden Orlando
English Learner Resource Teacher
Mission Bay High School
San Diego, California

Dr. Virginia Rojas
Language Education Consultant

Jody Talkington
English Language Learner Specialist
Oakland International High School
Oakland, California

SPRINGBOARD ENGLISH LANGUAGE DEVELOPMENT

Lori O'Dea
Executive Director
Content Development

Doug Waugh
Executive Director
Product Management

JoEllen Victoreen
English Language Arts
Instructional Manager

Sarah Balistreri
English Language Arts Editor

Jennifer Duva
English Language Arts Editor

Rebecca Grudzina
English Language Arts Editor

Melissa Ragan
English Language
Development Editor

Spencer Gonçalves
Assistant ELA Editor

Jessica Pippin
Assistant ELA Editor

Contents

Unit 1 Stories of Change: Analyzing and Creating Narratives

Part One: Personal Narrative: "The Jacket" by Gary Soto

Part Two: Short Story: "Thank You, M'am" by Langston Hughes

Part Three: Short Story: "Eleven" from *Woman Hollering Creek and Other Stories* by Sandra Cisneros

Unit 2   The Power To Change: Analyzing Literature and Creating Expository Text

Part One: Novel: Excerpt from *Walk Two Moons* by Sharon Creech

Part Two: Memoir: Excerpt from *Travels with Charley* by John Steinbeck

Part Three: Autobiography: "Dogs Make Us Human" from *Animals in Translation* by Temple Grandin and Catherine Johnson

Unit 3 Changing Perspectives: Analyzing and Creating Arguments

Part One: Editorial: "Don't Ban Peanuts" by the *Des Moines Register* Editorial Board

Part Two: News Article: "Most Dangerous 'Sport' of All May Be Cheerleading" by Lisa Ling and Arash Ghadishah

Part Three: Letter: "The First Americans" by Scott H. Peters, Grand Council Fire of American Indians

Unit 4 The Final Act: Analyzing and Performing Shakespeare

Part One: Informational Text: "Shakespeare's Life" from The British Library

Part Two: Poetry: "Oranges" by Gary Soto

Part Three: Drama: from *The Taming of the Shrew* by William Shakespeare

To the Student

Dear Student,

In the United States, the number of students whose first language is one other than English has grown. More and more students like you face the challenge of achieving academic success while continuing to develop their English skills.

While this is a big challenge, SpringBoard believes <u>you can do it!</u>

We designed this course to help you. Research shows that students who understand how English works, and who practice English in meaningful interactions can make huge gains. These gains lead to success in middle school courses as well as in high school, and eventually in the college and career choices you'll make.

In SpringBoard English Language Development, you will build your language in four key ways. You will:

- Study language that helps you understand English language arts.
- Learn academic vocabulary, so you can express yourself in any class.
- Identify the meaning of language that you may encounter in the texts you'll read.
- Use skills that will help you figure out the meaning of unknown or multiple meaning words when you read on your own.

The primary goal of SpringBoard English Language Development is to build your English language, and we hope that you will make this your goal, too.

Another goal is for you to become a stronger reader who can make meaning from even the most challenging texts that you read. In SpringBoard English Language Development, you will spend more time with each text, returning to it while engaging in interactive activities with your classmates. Your teacher will lead you in close reading sessions, during which you will zoom in on complex parts of a text to increase your understanding.

In addition to the language and reading goals, SpringBoard English Language Development wants you to speak and listen to your peers about the texts you're reading, their themes, and, of course, your own ideas. Most importantly, while you are in discussions with your classmates, you will learn how to support your opinions and ideas with evidence, add details, and produce the effect you want by choosing just the right words. In addition to frequent academic conversations, you will also have the opportunity to plan, prepare for, practice, and deliver presentations and performances.

Every day in SpringBoard English Language Development you will be writing. Sometimes you will be jotting down notes after a conversation or annotating a text as you read. Sometimes you will be adding words and phrases to a graphic organizer. Other times you will be completing sentences or writing your own sentences. You will be writing short summaries and explanations. You will also be crafting longer arguments, as well as creating narratives of your own. You will do all of these kinds of writing with the collaboration and support of your peers and your teacher. Working together, you will inspire and help each other to achieve the best results.

A final goal for SpringBoard English Language Development is for you to achieve something beyond the classroom—beyond the ELD classroom, that is. All the work you will be doing—building your language, analyzing complex texts, expressing and defending your ideas in discussions, writing arguments, explanations, and stories, and presenting your work to your peers—will help you to achieve success in another class: SpringBoard English Language Arts. What you learn in the ELD class will prepare you with the language resources you need to achieve at the highest levels.

The challenge is yours and we hope you will accept the challenge!

Sincerely,

SpringBoard

California English Language Development Standards

Part I: Interacting in Meaningful Ways

Communicative Modes	Standard Code	Emerging	Expanding	Bridging
Collaborative	PI.6.1	**Exchanging information/ideas** Engage in conversational exchanges and express ideas on familiar topics by asking and answering *yes–no* and *wh-* questions and responding using simple phrases.	**Exchanging information/ideas** Contribute to class, group, and partner discussions by following turn-taking rules, asking relevant questions, affirming others, adding relevant information, and paraphrasing key ideas.	**Exchanging information/ideas** Contribute to class, group, and partner discussions by following turn-taking rules, asking relevant questions, affirming others, adding relevant information and evidence, paraphrasing key ideas, building on responses, and providing useful feedback.
	PI.6.2	**Interacting via written English** Engage in short written exchanges with peers and collaborate on simple written texts on familiar topics, using technology when appropriate.	**Interacting via written English** Engage in longer written exchanges with peers and collaborate on more detailed written texts on a variety of topics, using technology when appropriate.	**Interacting via written English** Engage in extended written exchanges with peers and collaborate on complex written texts on a variety of topics, using technology when appropriate.
	PI.6.3	**Supporting opinions and persuading others** Negotiate with or persuade others in conversations (e.g., to gain and hold the floor or ask for clarification) using basic learned phrases (e.g., *I think ... , Would you please repeat that?*), as well as open responses.	**Supporting opinions and persuading others** Negotiate with or persuade others in conversations (e.g., to provide counter-arguments) using an expanded set of learned phrases (*I agree with X, but ...*), as well as open responses.	**Supporting opinions and persuading others** Negotiate with or persuade others in conversations using appropriate register (e.g., to reflect on multiple perspectives) using a variety of learned phrases, indirect reported speech (e.g., *I heard you say X, and Gabriel just pointed out Y*), as well as open responses.
	PI.6.4	**Adapting language choices** Adjust language choices according to social setting (e.g., classroom, break time) and audience (e.g., peers, teacher).	**Adapting language choices** Adjust language choices according to purpose (e.g., explaining, persuading, entertaining), task, and audience.	**Adapting language choices** Adjust language choices according to task (e.g., facilitating a science experiment, providing peer feedback on a writing assignment), purpose, task, and audience.

Communicative Modes	Standard Code	Emerging	Expanding	Bridging
Interpretive	PI.6.5	**Listening actively** Demonstrate active listening in oral presentation activities by asking and answering basic questions with prompting and substantial support.	**Listening actively** Demonstrate active listening in oral presentation activities by asking and answering detailed questions with occasional prompting and moderate support.	**Listening actively** Demonstrate active listening in oral presentation activities by asking and answering detailed questions with minimal prompting and support.
	PI.6.6a	**Reading/viewing closely** Explain ideas, phenomena, processes, and text relationships (e.g., compare/contrast, cause/effect, problem/solution) based on close reading of a variety of grade-level texts and viewing of multimedia with substantial support.	**Reading/viewing closely** Explain ideas, phenomena, processes, and text relationships (e.g., compare/contrast, cause/effect, problem/solution) based on close reading of a variety of grade-level texts and viewing of multimedia with moderate support.	**Reading/viewing closely** Explain ideas, phenomena, processes, and text relationships (e.g., compare/contrast, cause/effect, problem/solution) based on close reading of a variety of grade-level texts and viewing of multimedia with light support.
	PI.6.6b	**Reading/viewing closely** Express inferences and conclusions drawn based on close reading of grade-level texts and viewing of multimedia using some frequently used verbs (e.g., *shows that, based on*).	**Reading/viewing closely** Express inferences and conclusions drawn based on close reading of grade-level texts and viewing of multimedia using a variety of verbs (e.g., *suggests that, leads to*).	**Reading/viewing closely** Express inferences and conclusions drawn based on close reading of grade-level texts and viewing of multimedia using a variety of precise academic verbs (e.g., *indicates that, influences*).
	PI.6.6c	**Reading/viewing closely** Use knowledge of morphology (e.g., affixes, roots, and base words), context, reference materials, and visual cues to determine the meaning of unknown and multiple-meaning words on familiar topics.	**Reading/viewing closely** Use knowledge of morphology (e.g., affixes, roots, and base words), context, reference materials, and visual cues to determine the meaning of unknown and multiple-meaning words on familiar and new topics.	**Reading/viewing closely** Use knowledge of morphology (e.g., affixes, roots, and base words), context, reference materials, and visual cues to determine the meaning, including figurative and connotative meanings, of unknown and multiple-meaning words on a variety of new topics.

Communicative Modes	Standard Code	Emerging	Expanding	Bridging
Interpretive	PI.6.7	**Evaluating language choices** Explain how well writers and speakers use language to support ideas and arguments with detailed evidence (e.g., identifying the precise vocabulary used to present evidence, or the phrasing used to signal a shift in meaning) with substantial support.	**Evaluating language choices** Explain how well writers and speakers use specific language to present ideas or support arguments and provide detailed evidence (e.g., showing the clarity of the phrasing used to present an argument) with moderate support.	**Evaluating language choices** Explain how well writers and speakers use specific language resources to present ideas or support arguments and provide detailed evidence (e.g., identifying the specific language used to present ideas and claims that are well supported and distinguishing them from those that are not) with light support.
	PI.6.8	**Analyzing language choices** Explain how phrasing or different common words with similar meaning (e.g., choosing to use the word *cheap* versus the phrase *a good saver*) produce different effects on the audience.	**Analyzing language choices** Explain how phrasing, different words with similar meaning (e.g., describing a character as *stingy* versus *economical*), or figurative language (e.g., *The room was depressed and gloomy.*) produce shades of meaning and different effects on the audience.	**Analyzing language choices** Explain how phrasing, different words with similar meaning (e.g., *stingy-economical-unwasteful-thrifty*), or figurative language (e.g., *The room was depressed and gloomy.*) produce shades of meaning, nuances, and different effects on the audience.
Productive	PI.6.9	**Presenting** Plan and deliver brief oral presentations on a variety of topics and content areas.	**Presenting** Plan and deliver longer oral presentations on a variety of topics and content areas, using details and evidence to support ideas.	**Presenting** Plan and deliver longer oral presentations on a variety of topics and content areas, using reasoning and evidence to support ideas, as well as growing understanding of register.
	PI.6.10a	**Writing** Write short literary and informational texts (e.g., an argument for protecting the rainforests) collaboratively (e.g., with peers) and independently.	**Writing** Write longer literary and informational texts (e.g., an argument for protecting the rainforests) collaboratively (e.g., with peers) and independently using appropriate text organization.	**Writing** Write longer and more detailed literary and informational texts (e.g., an argument for protecting the rainforests) collaboratively (e.g., with peers) and independently using appropriate text organization and growing understanding of register.

Communicative Modes	Standard Code	Emerging	Expanding	Bridging
Productive	PI.6.11a	**Justifying/arguing** Justify opinions by providing some textual evidence (e.g., quoting from the text) or relevant background knowledge with substantial support.	**Justifying/arguing** Justify opinions or persuade others by providing relevant textual evidence (e.g., quoting from the text or referring to what the text says) or relevant background knowledge with moderate support.	**Justifying/arguing** Justify opinions or persuade others by providing detailed and relevant textual evidence (e.g., quoting from the text directly or referring to specific textual evidence) or relevant background knowledge with light support.
	PI.6.11b	**Justifying/arguing** Express attitude and opinions or temper statements with some basic modal expressions (e.g., *can, has to*).	**Justifying/arguing** Express attitude and opinions or temper statements with a variety of familiar modal expressions (e.g., *maybe/probably, can/could, must*).	**Justifying/arguing** Express attitude and opinions or temper statements with nuanced modal expressions (e.g., *probably/certainly/definitely, should/would, might*) and phrasing (e.g., *In my opinion ...*).
	PI.6.12a	**Selecting language resources** Use a select number of general academic words (e.g., *author, chart*) and domain-specific words (e.g., *scene, cell, fraction*) to create some precision while speaking and writing.	**Selecting language resources** Use a growing set of academic words (e.g., *author, chart, global, affect*), domain-specific words (e.g., *scene, setting, plot, point of view, fraction, cell membrane, democracy*), synonyms, and antonyms to create precision and shades of meaning while speaking and writing.	**Selecting language resources** Use an expanded set of general academic words (e.g., *affect, evidence, demonstrate, reluctantly*), domain-specific words (e.g., *scene, setting, plot, point of view, fraction, cell membrane, democracy*), synonyms, antonyms, and figurative language to create precision and shades of meaning while speaking and writing.
	PI.6.12b	**Selecting language resources** Use knowledge of morphology to appropriately select affixes in basic ways (e.g., *She likes* X.).	**Selecting language resources** Use knowledge of morphology to appropriately select affixes in a growing number of ways to manipulate language (e.g., *She likes* X. *That's impossible.*).	**Selecting language resources** Use knowledge of morphology to appropriately select affixes in a variety of ways to manipulate language (e.g., changing *observe ····> observation, reluctant ····> reluctantly, produce ····> production*, etc.).

Part II: Learning About How English Works

Language Processes	Standard Code	Emerging	Expanding	Bridging
Structuring Cohesive Texts	PII.6.1	**Understanding text structure** Apply basic understanding of how different text types are organized to express ideas (e.g., how a narrative is organized sequentially with predictable stages versus how arguments are organized around ideas) to comprehending texts and writing basic texts.	**Understanding text structure** Apply growing understanding of how different text types are organized to express ideas (e.g., how a narrative is organized sequentially with predictable stages versus how arguments are structured logically around reasons and evidence) to comprehending texts and writing texts with increasing cohesion.	**Understanding text structure** Apply increasing understanding of how different text types are organized to express ideas (e.g., how a historical account is organized chronologically versus how arguments are structured logically around reasons and evidence) to comprehending texts and writing cohesive texts.
	PII.6.2a	**Understanding cohesion** Apply basic understanding of language resources for referring the reader back or forward in text (e.g., how pronouns refer back to nouns in text) to comprehending texts and writing basic texts.	**Understanding cohesion** Apply growing understanding of language resources for referring the reader back or forward in text (e.g., how pronouns or synonyms refer back to nouns in text) to comprehending texts and writing texts with increasing cohesion.	**Understanding cohesion** Apply increasing understanding of language resources for referring the reader back or forward in text (e.g., how pronouns, synonyms, or nominalizations refer back to nouns in text) to comprehending texts and writing cohesive texts.
	PII.6.2b	**Understanding cohesion** Apply basic understanding of how ideas, events, or reasons are linked throughout a text using a select set of everyday connecting words or phrases (e.g., *first/next, at the beginning*) to comprehending texts and writing basic texts.	**Understanding cohesion** Apply growing understanding of how ideas, events, or reasons are linked throughout a text using a variety of connecting words or phrases (e.g., *for example, in the first place, as a result, on the other hand*) to comprehending texts and writing texts with increasing cohesion.	**Understanding cohesion** Apply increasing understanding of how ideas, events, or reasons are linked throughout a text using an increasing variety of academic connecting and transitional words or phrases (e.g., *consequently, specifically, however, moreover*) to comprehending texts and writing cohesive texts.

Language Processes	Standard Code	Emerging	Expanding	Bridging
Expanding and Enriching Ideas	PII.6.3	**Using verbs and verb phrases** Use a variety of verb types (e.g., doing, saying, being/having, thinking/feeling), tenses (e.g., present, past, future), and aspects (e.g., simple, progressive) appropriate for the text type and discipline (e.g., simple past and past progressive for recounting an experience) on familiar topics.	**Using verbs and verb phrases** Use various verb types (e.g., doing, saying, being/having, thinking/feeling, reporting), tenses (e.g., present, past, future), and aspects (e.g., simple, progressive, perfect) appropriate for the task, text type, and discipline (e.g., simple present for literary analysis) on an increasing variety of topics.	**Using verbs and verb phrases** Use various verb types (e.g., doing, saying, being/having, thinking/feeling, reporting), tenses (e.g., present, past, future), and aspects (e.g., simple, progressive, perfect) appropriate for the task, text type, and discipline (e.g., the present perfect to describe previously made claims or conclusions) on a variety of topics.
	PII.6.4	**Using nouns and noun phrases** Expand noun phrases in simple ways (e.g., adding a sensory adjective to a noun) in order to enrich the meaning of sentences and add details about ideas, people, things, etc.	**Using nouns and noun phrases** Expand noun phrases in a variety of ways (e.g., adding comparative/superlative adjectives to noun phrases or simple clause embedding) in order to enrich the meaning of sentences and add details about ideas, people, things, etc.	**Using nouns and noun phrases** Expand noun phrases in an increasing variety of ways (e.g., adding comparative/superlative and general academic adjectives to noun phrases or more complex clause embedding) in order to enrich the meaning of sentences and add details about ideas, people, things, etc.
	PII.6.5	**Modifying to add details** Expand sentences with simple adverbials (e.g., adverbs, adverb phrases, prepositional phrases) to provide details (e.g., time, manner, place, cause) about a familiar activity or process.	**Modifying to add details** Expand sentences with an increasing variety of adverbials (e.g., adverbs, adverb phrases, prepositional phrases) to provide details (e.g., time, manner, place, cause) about a familiar or new activity or process.	**Modifying to add details** Expand sentences with a variety of adverbials (e.g., adverbs, adverb phrases and clauses, prepositional phrases) to provide details (e.g., time, manner, place, cause) about a variety of familiar and new activities and processes.

Language Processes	Standard Code	Emerging	Expanding	Bridging
Connecting and Condensing Ideas	PII.6.6	**Connecting ideas** Combine clauses in a few basic ways to make connections between and join ideas (e.g., creating compound sentences using *and, but, so*).	**Connecting ideas** Combine clauses in an increasing variety of ways (e.g., creating compound and complex sentences) to make connections between and join ideas, for example, to express a reason (e.g., *He stayed at home on Sunday to study for Monday's exam*) or to make a concession (e.g., *She studied all night even though she wasn't feeling well*).	**Connecting ideas** Combine clauses in a wide variety of ways (e.g., creating compound and complex sentences) to make connections between and join ideas, for example, to express a reason (e.g., *He stayed at home on Sunday to study for Monday's exam*), to make a concession (e.g., *She studied all night even though she wasn't feeling well*), or to link two ideas that happen at the same time (e.g., *The students worked in groups while their teacher walked around the room*).
	PII.6.7	**Condensing ideas** Condense ideas in simple ways (e.g., by compounding verbs, adding prepositional phrases, or through simple embedded clauses or other ways of condensing as in, This is a story about a girl. The girl changed the world. ····⟩ This is a story about a girl *who changed the world*.) to create precise and detailed sentences.	**Condensing ideas** Condense ideas in an increasing variety of ways (e.g., through various types of embedded clauses and other ways of condensing, as in, Organic vegetables are food. They're made without chemical fertilizers. They're made without chemical insecticides. ····⟩ Organic vegetables are foods *that are made without chemical fertilizers or insecticides*.) to create precise and detailed sentences.	**Condensing ideas** Condense ideas in a variety of ways (e.g., through various types of embedded clauses, ways of condensing, and nominalization as in, They *destroyed* the rainforest. Lots of animals *died*. ····⟩ The *destruction* of the rainforest led to the *death* of many animals.) to create precise and detailed sentences.
Foundational Literacy Skills: **Literacy in an Alphabetic Writing System** • Print concepts Phonological awareness • Phonics & word recognition • Fluency	PIII.6	**See Appendix A [of the California ELD Standards] for information on teaching reading foundational skills to English learners of various profiles based on age, native language, native language writing system, schooling experience, and literacy experience and proficiency. Some considerations are:** • Native language and literacy (e.g., phoneme awareness or print concept skills in native language) should be assessed for potential transference to English language and literacy. • Similarities between native language and English should be highlighted (e.g., phonemes or letters that are the same in both languages). • Differences between native language and English should be highlighted (e.g., some phonemes in English may not exist in the student's native language; native language syntax may be different from English syntax).		

California Common Core State Standards

Reading Standards for Literature

Key Ideas and Details	RL.6.1	Cite textual evidence to support analysis of what the text says explicitly as well as inferences drawn from the text.
	RL.6.2	Determine a theme or central idea of a text and how it is conveyed through particular details; provide a summary of the text distinct from personal opinions or judgments.
	RL.6.3	Describe how a particular story's or drama's plot unfolds in a series of episodes as well as how the characters respond or change as the plot moves toward a resolution.
Craft and Structure	RL.6.4	Determine the meaning of words and phrases as they are used in a text, including figurative and connotative meanings; analyze the impact of a specific word choice on meaning and tone. **(See grade 6 Language standards 4–6 for additional expectations.) CA**
	RL.6.5	Analyze how a particular sentence, chapter, scene, or stanza fits into the overall structure of a text and contributes to the development of the theme, setting, or plot.
	RL.6.6	Explain how an author develops the point of view of the narrator or speaker in a text.
Integration of Knowledge and Ideas	RL.6.7	Compare and contrast the experience of reading a story, drama, or poem to listening to or viewing an audio, video, or live version of the text, including contrasting what they "see" and "hear" when reading the text to what they perceive when they listen or watch.
	RL.6.8	(Not applicable to literature)
	RL.6.9	Compare and contrast texts in different forms or genres (e.g., stories and poems; historical novels and fantasy stories) in terms of their approaches to similar themes and topics.
Range of Reading and Text Complexity	RL.6.10	By the end of the year, read and comprehend literature, including stories, dramas, and poems, in the grades 6–8 text complexity band proficiently, with scaffolding as needed at the high end of the range.

Reading Standards for Informational Text

Key Ideas and Details	RI.6.1	Cite textual evidence to support analysis of what the text says explicitly as well as inferences drawn from the text.
	RI.6.2	Determine a central idea of a text and how it is conveyed through particular details; provide a summary of the text distinct from personal opinions or judgments.
	RI.6.3	Analyze in detail how a key individual, event, or idea is introduced, illustrated, and elaborated in a text (e.g., through examples or anecdotes)
Craft and Structure	RI.6.4	Determine the meaning of words and phrases as they are used in a text, including figurative, connotative, and technical meanings. **(See grade 6 Language standards 4–6 for additional expectations.) CA**
	RI.6.5	Analyze how a particular sentence, paragraph, chapter, or section fits into the overall structure of a text and contributes to the development of the ideas.
	RI.6.5a	**Analyze the use of text features (e.g., graphics, headers, captions) in popular media. CA**
	RI.6.6	Determine an author's point of view or purpose in a text and explain how it is conveyed in the text.
Integration of Knowledge and Ideas	RI.6.7	Integrate information presented in different media or formats (e.g., visually, quantitatively) as well as in words to develop a coherent understanding of a topic or issue.
	RI.6.8	Trace and evaluate the argument and specific claims in a text, distinguishing claims that are supported by reasons and evidence from claims that are not.
	RI.6.9	Compare and contrast one author's presentation of events with that of another (e.g., a memoir written by and a biography on the same person).
Range of Reading and Text Complexity	RI.6.10	By the end of the year, read and comprehend literary nonfiction in the grades 6–8 text complexity band proficiently, with scaffolding as needed at the high end of the range.

Writing Standards

Text Types and Purposes	W.6.1	Write arguments to support claims with clear reasons and relevant evidence.
	W.6.1a	Introduce claim(s) and organize the reasons and evidence clearly.
	W.6.1b	Support claim(s) with clear reasons and relevant evidence, using credible sources and demonstrating an understanding of the topic or text.
	W.6.1c	Use words, phrases, and clauses to clarify the relationships among claim(s) and reasons.
	W.6.1d	Establish and maintain a formal style.
	W.6.1e	Provide a concluding statement or section that follows from the argument presented.
	W.6.2	Write informative/explanatory texts to examine a topic and convey ideas, concepts, and information through the selection, organization, and analysis of relevant content.
	W.6.2a	Introduce a topic **or thesis statement**; organize ideas, concepts, and information, using strategies such as definition, classification, comparison/contrast, and cause/effect; include formatting (e.g., headings), graphics (e.g., charts, tables), and multimedia when useful to aiding comprehension. **CA**
	W.6.2b	Develop the topic with relevant facts, definitions, concrete details, quotations, or other information and examples.
	W.6.2c	Use appropriate transitions to clarify the relationships among ideas and concepts.
	W.6.2d	Use precise language and domain-specific vocabulary to inform about or explain the topic.
	W.6.2e	Establish and maintain a formal style.
	W.6.2f	Provide a concluding statement or section that follows from the information or explanation presented.
	W.6.3	Write narratives to develop real or imagined experiences or events using effective technique, relevant descriptive details, and well-structured event sequences.
	W.6.3a	Engage and orient the reader by establishing a context and introducing a narrator and/or characters; organize an event sequence that unfolds naturally and logically.
	W.6.3b	Use narrative techniques, such as dialogue, pacing, and description, to develop experiences, events, and/or characters.
	W.6.3c	Use a variety of transition words, phrases, and clauses to convey sequence and signal shifts from one time frame or setting to another.

Writing Standards

Text Types and Purposes	W.6.3d	Use precise words and phrases, relevant descriptive details, and sensory language to convey experiences and events.
	W.6.3e	Provide a conclusion that follows from the narrated experiences or events.
Production and Distribution of Writing	W.6.4	Produce clear and coherent writing in which the development, organization, and style are appropriate to task, purpose, and audience. (Grade-specific expectations for writing types are defined in standards 1–3 above.)
	W.6.5	With some guidance and support from peers and adults, develop and strengthen writing as needed by planning, revising, editing, rewriting, or trying a new approach. (Editing for conventions should demonstrate command of Language standards 1–3 up to and including grade 6.)
	W.6.6	Use technology, including the Internet, to produce and publish writing as well as to inter act and collaborate with others; demonstrate sufficient command of keyboarding skills to type a minimum of three pages in a single sitting.
Research to Build and Present Knowledge	W.6.7	Conduct short research projects to answer a question, drawing on several sources and refocusing the inquiry when appropriate.
	W.6.8	Gather relevant information from multiple print and digital sources; assess the credibility of each source; and quote or paraphrase the data and conclusions of others while avoiding plagiarism and providing basic bibliographic information for sources.
	W.6.9	Draw evidence from literary or informational texts to support analysis, reflection, and research.
	W.6.9a	Apply *grade 6 Reading standards* to literature (e.g., "Compare and contrast texts in different forms or genres [e.g., stories and poems; historical novels and fantasy stories] in terms of their approaches to similar themes and topics").
	W.6.9b	Apply *grade 6 Reading standards* to literary nonfiction (e.g., "Trace and evaluate the argument and specific claims in a text, distinguishing claims that are supported by reasons and evidence from claims that are not").
Range of Writing	W.6.10	Write routinely over extended time frames (time for research, reflection, and revision) and shorter time frames (a single sitting or a day or two) for a range of discipline-specific tasks, purposes, and audiences.

Speaking and Listening Standards

Comprehension and Collaboration	SL.6.1	Engage effectively in a range of collaborative discussions (one-on-one, in groups, and teacher-led) with diverse partners on *grade 6 topics, texts, and issues*, building on others' ideas and expressing their own clearly.
	SL.6.1a	Come to discussions prepared, having read or studied required material; explicitly draw on that preparation by referring to evidence on the topic, text, or issue to probe and reflect on ideas under discussion.
	SL.6.1b	Follow rules for collegial discussions, set specific goals and deadlines, and define individual roles as needed.
	SL.6.1c	Pose and respond to specific questions with elaboration and detail by making comments that contribute to the topic, text, or issue under discussion.
	SL.6.1d	Review the key ideas expressed and demonstrate understanding of multiple perspectives through reflection and paraphrasing.
	SL.6.2	Interpret information presented in diverse media and formats (e.g., visually, quantitatively, orally) and explain how it contributes to a topic, text, or issue under study.
	SL.6.3	Delineate a speaker's argument and specific claims, distinguishing claims that are supported by reasons and evidence from claims that are not.
Presentation of Knowledge and Ideas	SL.6.4	Present claims and findings **(e.g., argument, narrative, informative, response to literature presentations)**, sequencing ideas logically and using pertinent descriptions, facts, and details **and nonverbal elements** to accentuate main ideas or themes; use appropriate eye contact, adequate volume, and clear pronunciation. **CA**
	SL.6.4a	**Plan and deliver an informative/explanatory presentation that develops a topic with relevant facts, definitions, and concrete details; uses appropriate transitions to clarify relationships; uses precise language and domain specific vocabulary; and provides a strong conclusion. CA**
	SL.6.5	Include multimedia components (e.g., graphics, images, music, sound) and visual displays in presentations to clarify information.
	SL.6.6	Adapt speech to a variety of contexts and tasks, demonstrating command of formal English when indicated or appropriate. (See grade 6 Language standards 1 and 3 for specific expectations.)

Language Standards

Conventions of Standard English	L.6.1	Demonstrate command of the conventions of standard English grammar and usage when writing or speaking.
	L.6.1a	Ensure that pronouns are in the proper case (subjective, objective, possessive).
	L.6.1b	Use **all pronouns, including** intensive pronouns (e.g., *myself, ourselves*) **correctly. CA**
	L.6.1c	Recognize and correct inappropriate shifts in pronoun number and person.
	L.6.1d	Recognize and correct vague pronouns (i.e., ones with unclear or ambiguous antecedents).
	L.6.1e	Recognize variations from standard English in their own and others' writing and speaking, and identify and use strategies to improve expression in conventional language.
	L.6.2	Demonstrate command of the conventions of standard English capitalization, punctuation, and spelling when writing.
	L.6.2a	Use punctuation (commas, parentheses, dashes) to set off nonrestrictive/ parenthetical elements.
	L.6.2b	Spell correctly.
Knowledge of Language	L.6.3	Use knowledge of language and its conventions when writing, speaking, reading, or listening.
	L.6.3a	Vary sentence patterns for meaning, reader/ listener interest, and style.
	L.6.3b	Maintain consistency in style and tone.
Vocabulary Acquisition and Use	L.6.4	Determine or clarify the meaning of unknown and multiple-meaning words and phrases based on *grade 6 reading and content*, choosing flexibly from a range of strategies.
	L.6.4a	Use context (e.g., the overall meaning of a sentence or paragraph; a word's position or function in a sentence) as a clue to the meaning of a word or phrase.
	L.6.4b	Use common, grade-appropriate Greek or Latin affixes and roots as clues to the meaning of a word (e.g., *audience, auditory, audible*).
	L.6.4c	Consult reference materials (e.g., dictionaries, glossaries, thesauruses), both print and digital, to find the pronunciation of a word or determine or clarify its precise meaning or its part of speech.
	L.6.4d	Verify the preliminary determination of the meaning of a word or phrase (e.g., by checking the inferred meaning in context or in a dictionary).

Language Standards

Vocabulary Acquisition and Use	L.6.5	Demonstrate understanding of figurative language, word relationships, and nuances in word meanings.
	L.6.5a	Interpret figures of speech (e.g., personification) in context.
	L.6.5b	Use the relationship between particular words (e.g., cause/effect, part/whole, item/category) to better understand each of the words.
	L.6.5c	Distinguish among the connotations (associations) of words with similar denotations (definitions) (e.g., *stingy, scrimping, economical, unwasteful, thrifty*).
	L.6.6	Acquire and use accurately grade-appropriate general academic and domain-specific words and phrases; gather vocabulary knowledge when considering a word or phrase important to comprehension or expression.

STORIES OF CHANGE:
Analyzing and Creating Narratives

Visual Prompt: A butterfly goes through several changes in its life. It starts as an egg, becomes a caterpillar and then a chrysalis, and finally emerges as a beautiful butterfly. In what ways do people change as they move through the stages of their lives?

Unit Overview

Unit 1 introduces the idea of "change" as the conceptual focus for the year. By reading, analyzing, and creating texts, you will examine changes that happen in your life as well as in the world around you. Through your responses to texts, you will better understand that change is threaded through all of our lives and is something we can tell stories about.

Selecting Language Resources

WORD CONNECTIONS

Cognates

The English word *indicate* and the Spanish word *indicar* are cognates. They both mean "to show," and come from the Latin verb *indicare*, meaning "to point out."

Learning Targets

- Develop language resources to use in one's speaking and writing about personal narratives.
- Use an expanded set of words to create precision while speaking and writing.
- Adjust language choices to suit the academic setting.

The chart presents words and phrases you will use in discussion and writing. Think about each word or phrase. Circle Q, H, or T to indicate how well you know it. Work with a partner, asking your partner to explain each word or phrase. Listen closely to the explanation, and then write your partner's name and condensed idea in the In Our Own Words column.

Rating	Q	H	T
	I have seen this word or phrase, but I have **questions** about its meaning.	I have **heard** this word or phrase, but I do not know it well.	I know this word or phrase so well that I could **teach** it to someone else.

Word or Phrase	Definition	In Our Own Words
personal narrative Rating Q H T	a story based on one's own life and told in the first-person point of view; describes an incident, and includes a response and a reflection on the incident	
character Rating Q H T	a person or animal in a story	
point of view Rating Q H T	the perspective from which a story is told	
first-person point of view Rating Q H T	the storytelling perspective in which the narrator is a character in the story telling what he or she sees or knows	
third-person point of view Rating Q H T	the storytelling perspective in which the narrator is someone outside the story	
figurative language Rating Q H T	imaginative language that is not meant to be interpreted literally, but to create an effect on the reader	
metaphor Rating Q H T	a comparison of two unlike things without using the words *like* or *as*	
simile Rating Q H T	a comparison of two unlike things using the words *like* or *as*	
incident Rating Q H T	the central piece of action that is the focus of the story	
response Rating Q H T	the immediate emotions and actions associated with the incident in a story	
reflection Rating Q H T	a description that explores the significance of the incident in a story	

Academic and Social Language Preview

Learning Target

● Develop knowledge of a growing set of academic and social vocabulary to comprehend when reading and to create precision and shades of meaning in one's own speaking and writing.

VOCABULARY PREVIEW

bikers: (noun) people who ride motorcycles

bob: (verb) to move down and up quickly, or nod repeatedly

camouflage: (noun) the green and brown clothing that soldiers and hunters wear that makes them harder to see

champ: (noun) short for champion; someone who has won a competition

couple: (noun) two people who are together by being in a romantic relationship or by marriage

embarrassed: (adjective) made to look or feel foolish in front of other people

ground: (noun) the solid surface of the earth

however: (adverb) on the other hand, by contrast

hurled: (verb) thrown with force

mirror: (noun) a smooth surface that reflects images

profile: (noun) the shape of a head or face as seen or drawn from the side

several: (adjective) more than two, but not very many

though: (conjunction) although, in spite of the fact that

Vocabulary Practice

Use the definitions in the Vocabulary Preview or a dictionary to support your work.

Practice 1. Circle the word or phrase whose meaning is closest to the meaning of the vocabulary word.

Vocabulary Word	Words or Phrases to Choose From
bob	move up and down move around move from side to side
camouflage	uniform decoration disguise
embarrassed	pleased ashamed frightened
hurled	threw dropped went fast
profile	seen from above seen from the front seen from the side
several	none a few many

Practice 2. Complete each sentence, paying attention to the **bold** vocabulary word.

1. He enjoyed the movie, **however**,

_____

2. **Though** the weather was hot and sunny, she wore

_____

Practice 3. Choose the best word to complete each sentence.

1. The woman stared into the _____, trying to see if paint had splashed onto her face. (mirror, ground)

2. The bird stared at the _____, looking for bugs to eat. (ground, mirror)

3. The _____ had invited several other married friends to their new house for dinner. (bikers, couple)

4. The girl thought that _____ were cool, so she desperately wanted a motorcycle jacket. (couples, bikers)

5. "Hey, _____," the coach said to the team. "You did a great job at practice today, and you deserve congratulations!" (bikers, champs)

Learning Targets
- Apply understanding of how personal narratives are structured to comprehending the text.
- Read closely and annotate the text to find the language resources an author uses to establish character, setting, and incident.

Read and Annotate

Read "The Jacket" and annotate the text as you read.

■ Use the My Notes area to write questions or ideas you have about the story.

■ Underline words and phrases that tell about the characters and setting.

■ Put a star next to the central incident.

■ Put exclamation marks next to the narrator's responses to the incident.

■ Circle unknown words and phrases.

Personal Narrative

The Jacket

by Gary Soto

1 My clothes have failed me. I remember the green coat that I wore in fifth and sixth grades when you either danced like a champ or pressed yourself against a greasy wall, bitter as a penny toward the happy couples.

2 When I needed a new jacket and my mother asked what kind I wanted, I described something like bikers wear: black leather and silver studs, with enough belts to hold down a small town. We were in the kitchen, steam on the windows from her cooking. She listened so long while stirring dinner that I thought she understood for sure the kind I wanted. The next day when I got home from school, I discovered draped on my bedpost a jacket the color of day-old guacamole. I threw my books on the bed and approached the jacket slowly, as if it were a stranger whose hand I had to shake. I touched the **vinyl** sleeve, the collar, and peeked at the mustard-colored lining.

3 From the kitchen mother yelled that my jacket was in the closet. I closed the door to her voice and pulled at the rack of clothes in the closet, hoping the jacket on the bedpost wasn't for me but my mean brother. No luck. I gave up. From my bed, I stared at the jacket. I wanted to cry because it was so ugly and so big that I knew I'd have to wear it a long time. I was a small kid, thin as a young tree, and it would be years before I'd have a new one. I stared at the jacket, like an enemy, thinking bad things before I took off my old jacket, whose sleeves climbed halfway to my elbow.

4 I put the big jacket on. I zipped it up and down several times, and rolled the cuffs up so they didn't cover my hands. I put my hands in the pockets and flapped the jacket like a bird's wings. I stood in front of the mirror, full face, then profile, and then looked over my shoulder as if someone had called me. I sat on the bed, stood against the bed, and combed my hair to see what I would look like doing something natural. I looked ugly. I threw it on my brother's bed and looked at it for a long time before I slipped it on and went out to the backyard, smiling a "thank

My Notes

vinyl: a plastic material

Why did his mom buy him an ugly jacket?

Interpret the Text Using Close Reading

My Notes

you" to my mom as I passed her in the kitchen. With my hands in my pockets I kicked a ball against the fence, and then climbed it to sit looking into the alley. I hurled orange peels at the mouth of an open garbage can, and when the peels were gone I watched the white puffs of my breath thin to nothing.

5   I jumped down, hands in my pockets, and in the backyard, on my knees, I teased my dog, Brownie, by swooping my arms while making birdcalls. He jumped at me and missed. He jumped again and again, until a tooth sunk deep, ripping an L-shaped tear on my left sleeve. I pushed Brownie away to study the tear as I would a cut on my arm. There was no blood, only a few loose pieces of fuzz. Damn dog, I thought, and pushed him away hard when he tried to bite again. I got up from my knees and went to my bedroom to sit with my jacket on my lap, with the lights out.

6   That was the first afternoon with my new jacket. The next day I wore it to sixth grade and got a D on a math quiz. During the morning recess Frankie T., the playground terrorist, pushed me to the ground and told me to stay there until recess was over. My best friend, Steve Negrete, ate an apple while looking at me, and the girls turned away to whisper on the monkey bars. The teachers were no help: they looked my way and talked about how foolish I looked in my new jacket. I saw their heads bob with laughter, their hands half covering their mouths.

7   Even though it was cold, I took off the jacket during lunch and played kickball in a thin shirt, my arms feeling like **braille** from goose bumps. But when I returned to class I slipped the jacket on and shivered until I was warm. I sat on my hands, heating them up, while my teeth chattered like a cup of crooked dice. Finally warm, I slid out of the jacket but put it back on a few minutes later when the fire bell rang. We paraded out into the yard where we, the sixth graders, walked past all the other grades to stand against the back fence. Everybody saw me. Although they didn't say out loud, "Man, that's ugly," I heard the buzz-buzz of gossip and even laughter that I knew was meant for me.

8   And so I went, in my guacamole-colored jacket. So embarrassed, so hurt, I couldn't even do my homework. I received C's on quizzes and forgot the state capitals and the rivers of South America, our friendly neighbor. Even the girls who had been friendly blew away like loose flowers to follow the boys in neat jackets.

9   I wore that thing for three years until the sleeves grew short and my forearms stuck out like the necks of turtles. All during that time no love came to me—no little dark girl in a Sunday dress she wore on Monday. At lunchtime I stayed with the ugly boys who leaned against the chainlink fence and looked around with propellers of grass spinning in our mouths. We saw girls walk by alone, saw couples, hand in hand, their heads like bookends pressing air together. We saw them and spun our **propellers** so fast our faces were blurs.

10   I blame that jacket for those bad years. I blame my mother for her bad taste and her cheap ways. It was a sad time for the heart. With a friend I spent my sixth-grade year in a tree in the alley, waiting for something good to happen to me in that jacket, which had become the ugly brother who tagged along wherever I went. And it was about that time that I began to grow. My chest puffed up with muscle and, strangely, a few more ribs. Even my hands, those fleshy hammers, showed bravely through the cuffs, the fingers already hardening for the coming fights. But that L-shaped rip on the left sleeve got bigger; bits of stuffing coughed out from its wound after a hard day of play. I finally Scotch-taped it closed, but in rain or cold weather the tape peeled off like a scab and more stuffing fell out until that sleeve shriveled into a **palsied** arm. That winter the elbows began to crack and whole chunks of green began to fall off. I showed the cracks to my mother, who always

braille: a system of writing for blind people that uses raised dots on a page to represent letters

propeller: an object with quickly turning blades

palsy: a condition featuring uncontrolled shaking of a body part

Interpret the Text Using Close Reading

seemed to be at the stove with steamed-up glasses, and she said that there were children in Mexico who would love that jacket. I told her that this was America and yelled that Debbie, my sister, didn't have a jacket like mine. I ran outside, ready to cry, and climbed the tree by the alley to think bad thoughts and watch my breath puff white and disappear.

11 But whole pieces still casually flew off my jacket when I played hard, read quietly, or took **vicious** spelling tests at school. When it became so spotted that my brother began to call me "camouflage," I flung it over the fence into the alley. Later, however, I swiped the jacket off the ground and went inside to drape it across my lap and **mope**.

12 I was called to dinner: steam silvered my mother's glasses as she said grace; my brother and sister with their heads bowed made ugly faces at their glasses of powdered milk. I gagged too, but eagerly ate big rips of buttered tortilla that held scooped-up beans. Finished, I went outside with my jacket across my arm. It was a cold sky. The faces of clouds were piled up, hurting. I climbed the fence, jumping down with a grunt. I started up the alley and soon slipped into my jacket, that green ugly brother who breathed over my shoulder that day and ever since.

My Notes

vicious: cruel and dangerous

mope: to feel aimless and unhappy

Interacting in Meaningful Ways: Academic Collaboration

Learning Targets

- Ask and answer questions about a personal narrative in collaborative conversations, demonstrating active listening, and drawing upon an expanding pool of language resources for discussing literature.

- Express and support opinions of a personal narrative in conversation.

Turn to your partner or small group to discuss each question about "The Jacket." After you have discussed a question, write notes about your answer before going on to the next question.

1. Who is the narrator of "The Jacket"? What do you learn about him?

> The narrator of the story is _____.

2. What is the central incident in the story? After discussing it, try to summarize it in one sentence.

> I think the central incident is _____.

3. What was the narrator's response to the central incident?

> The narrator responds to the incident by acting/feeling _____.

4. In paragraph 2, what words does the narrator use to describe the jacket? How do these words help you understand how he feels about the jacket?

> The words _____ are effective because _____.

Asking Questions

Personal narratives often end with a reflection on the central incident. With your partner or small group, read aloud the ending of "The Jacket," paragraphs 10–12. Discuss what questions you have about the ending. Write one question to share with the whole class.

_____

_____

How English Works: Pronouns and Point of View

Learning Target

● Apply understanding of first- and third-person pronouns to comprehending and writing texts.

The Narrative Point of View

"The Jacket" is a personal narrative written in the first-person point of view. The narrator is a character in the story, telling about an incident in his life and how he responded to it. The narrator uses first-person pronouns to refer to himself.

⚙ Language Resources: Pronouns

	Subjective (Subject)		Objective (Object)		Possessive	
	Singular	**Plural**	**Singular**	**Plural**	**Singular**	**Plural**
First-person	I	we	me	us	mine, my*	ours, our*
Third-person	he, she, it	they	him, her, it	them	his, hers, her*, its	theirs, their*

*These related words are possessive adjectives, not pronouns.

Skim through "The Jacket," looking for sentences you like that have first-person pronouns. Write three example sentences in the chart. Then rewrite each sentence in the third-person point of view using the correct pronouns. Use the Language Resources: Pronouns chart for support.

First-person sentences from "The Jacket"	Rewrite in the third-person point of view
My clothes have failed **me**.	**His** clothes have failed **him**.

 **Quick Conversation**

● Share your work with a partner. Read aloud the original and revised sentences. Discuss how they compare and which sentences you prefer. What is the effect of writing in the first-person point of view compared to the third-person point of view? Record notes from your discussion.

> In my opinion, the _____-person sentences sound _____.

> I prefer the _____-person sentences because _____.

> I think the _____-person sentences are effective because _____.

Present a Narrative

Now that you have analyzed and evaluated pronouns and point of view in "The Jacket," write two versions of a brief narrative in which you describe something that happened at school recently. First, write your narrative in the third-person point of view, as though you are writing about yourself as a character in a story. Use third-person pronouns: "He/she arrived late to school that morning." Write your narrative a second time, using the first-person point of view and first-person pronouns: "I arrived late to school that morning." Read each of your narratives aloud, and ask your listeners to identify which point of view was more effective. Use the following space to write your narratives.

_____

_____

_____

_____

_____

_____

_____

_____

_____

Interacting in Meaningful Ways:
Analyze Figurative Language

Learning Targets

- Analyze and explain in conversation and writing how figurative language produces effects on the reader.

- Evaluate and explain in conversation and writing how effectively the author uses figurative language.

- Express and justify opinions in conversation and writing by providing text evidence and using nuanced modal expressions and phrases.

Figurative Language

Gary Soto, the author of "The Jacket," uses figurative language to create effects by engaging the reader's imagination. In this activity, you will identify, analyze, and evaluate figurative language.

Skim through "The Jacket" looking for examples of similes and metaphors. Write four examples in the chart. Then analyze each example to understand the effect the author is trying to create. Finally, evaluate the simile or metaphor by choosing one adverb from the Language Resources list to express how effective you think the simile or metaphor is.

Simile or Metaphor	Analyze the Effect	Evaluate How Effective It Is
simile: bitter as a penny	A penny is small, worth very little, and tastes bitter. The narrator felt worthless and bitter.	definitely

Language Resources

Literary Terms

Figurative Language: imaginative language that is not meant to be interpreted literally, but to create an effect on the reader

Simile: a comparison of two unlike things using the words *like* or *as*

Metaphor: a comparison of two unlike things without using the words *like* or *as*

ACADEMIC VOCABULARY

Effective is an adjective that can provide detail about, or modify, a noun or pronoun. Something that is described as effective produces an **effect** or result. Something that is not effective can be described as **ineffective**.

Language Resources

Modal Adverbs

Adverbs add detail to, or modify, verbs, adjectives, and adverbs. The following adverbs are examples that you can use to express how effective something is.

High
definitely absolutely highly

Medium
probably apparently somewhat

Low
possibly perhaps maybe

 **Quick Conversation**

● Share your work with a partner. Take turns explaining your analysis and evaluation of the similes and metaphors. Discuss whether your partner agrees or disagrees with your evaluation. Record notes from your discussion.

> In my opinion, this simile is _____ effective because _____.

> Do you agree with my analysis/evaluation?

> I agree/disagree with your analysis because _____.

> I agree/disagree with your evaluation because _____.

Write a Short Argument

After analyzing and evaluating figurative language in "The Jacket," you have enough information to write a short argument. Choose one simile or metaphor from your chart. Write a short argument in which you explain the meaning of the simile or metaphor, state your opinion of how effective it is, and give a reason why. Before writing, read the model short argument provided. Notice what information is in each of the four sentences. Try structuring your argument in the same way.

_____

_____

_____

_____

MODEL: SHORT ARGUMENT

The narrator uses the simile "bitter as a penny" to describe how he felt at school dances. A penny is small, worth very little, and has a bitter taste. This simile tells the reader that the narrator felt bitter and worthless. In my opinion, this simile is definitely effective because it makes the reader understand exactly how the narrator felt.

Interacting in Meaningful Ways: Writing a Personal Narrative

Learning Targets

- Express and justify opinions about a personal narrative in conversation and writing by providing text evidence or relevant background knowledge.
- Write the incident and response of a personal narrative.
- Use figurative language effectively to create precision and shades of meaning while writing.

Review your annotations and notes on "The Jacket" and use them to complete the graphic organizer.

Incident	Response	Reflection
What is the central action that is the focus of the story?	What emotions and actions resulted from the incident?	What was the significance of the incident? How did the narrator learn or grow from it?

 Language Resources

personal narrative: a story based on one's own life and told in the first-person point of view; describes an **incident**, and includes a response and a reflection on the incident

incident: the central piece of action that is the focus of the narrative

response: the immediate emotions and actions associated with the incident in a story

reflection: a description that explores the significance of the incident in a story

Quick Conversation

Share your work with your partner. Compare your ideas about the incident, response, and reflection.

Next, read aloud the last sentence of the story:

> I started up the alley and soon slipped into my jacket, that green ugly brother who breathed over my shoulder that day and ever since.

Discuss the sentence. What does it tell you about the narrator and why the incident of "The Jacket" was important to him? Record notes from your discussion.

I think the incident was important to the narrator because ____.

I agree/disagree because ____.

Based on ____, I think ____.

_____

_____

_____

Will you please explain that?

Planning the Incident and Response of a Personal Narrative

Use the graphic organizer to plan your own incident and response of a personal narrative. Think about an important event in your life, and make notes about it in reponse to the questions that follow.

Incident	Response
What is the central action that is the focus of your story?	**How did you feel and what did you do as a result of the incident?**

1. Think about your incident.
2. Talk to your partner about what you want to write.
3. Write down your story. Use first-person point of view. Use simile. Use transitions.
4. Have your partner read it.

Narrative Writing Prompt

Write a draft of your personal narrative. Be sure to:

■ Establish the incident (setting, conflict, character).

■ Describe the response (feelings and actions).

■ Write from the first-person point of view and include details about the narrator's and other characters' feelings.

■ Use figurative language such as similes and metaphors to let readers know how the narrator feels.

_____

_____

_____

_____

_____

_____

_____

_____

Selecting Language Resources

Learning Targets

- Develop language resources to use in one's own speaking and writing about short stories.
- Use an expanded set of words to create precision while speaking and writing.
- Adjust language choices to suit the academic setting.

The chart presents words and phrases you will use in discussion and writing. Think about each word or phrase. Circle Q, H, or T to indicate how well you know it. Work with a partner, asking your partner to explain each word or phrase. Listen closely to the explanation, and then write your partner's name and condensed idea in the In Our Own Words column.

WORD CONNECTIONS

Roots and Affixes

The suffix -*tion* turns verbs, or action words, into nouns. For example, when the suffix is added to the verb *emote*, a new word is formed. *Emote* means "to express a feeling." *Emotion* means "a strong feeling, such as love or fear."

Rating	Q	H	T
	I have seen this word or phrase, but I have **questions** about its meaning.	I have **heard** this word or phrase, but do not know it well.	I know this word or phrase so well that I could **teach** it to someone else.

Word or Phrase	Definition	In Our Own Words
short story Rating Q H T	a short work of fiction; plot structure includes rising action, climax, falling action, and resolution	
theme Rating Q H T	the main subject or message being written about in a story	
structure Rating Q H T	the way in which a story is organized	
plot Rating Q H T	the series of events that make up a story	
rising action Rating Q H T	the main events that form the plot of a story; these events lead to the story's climax	
climax Rating Q H T	the most exciting or important part of a story; the turning point	
falling action Rating Q H T	the events that lead to the ending of a story	
resolution Rating Q H T	the point at the end of the story when the theme is revealed	
external conflict Rating Q H T	a conflict in which the character struggles with an outside force, such as another person or something in nature	
internal conflict Rating Q H T	a conflict in which the character struggles with something inside himself or herself, such as the character's desires or emotions	

Academic and Social Language Preview

Learning Target

- Develop knowledge of a growing set of academic and social vocabulary to comprehend when reading and to create precision and shades of meaning in one's own speaking and writing.

VOCABULARY PREVIEW

contact: (noun) when two people or things physically touch each other

furnished: (adjective) supplied with furniture

have a great mind to: (idiom) be strongly inclined to

least: (noun) the smallest thing that someone can do

mistrust: (verb) to have no trust in, to be suspicious of

nor: (conjunction) used after a negative statement to add a related negative statement

pause: (noun) a short time when something is stopped before starting again

release: (verb) to set free, to let go of

right square: (idiom) in the very center of

roomers: (noun) people who rent rooms in other people's houses

struggle: (verb) to try hard to move yourself

unless: (preposition) except possibly

Vocabulary Practice

Practice 1. Circle the word or phrase whose meaning is closest to the meaning of the vocabulary word.

Vocabulary Word	Words or Phrases to Choose From
contact	separation touch avoidance
furnished	with furniture without furniture to rent furniture
least	the largest amount just enough the smallest amount
mistrust	feel trust in have suspicions about be fooled by
pause	break continuation end
release	let go hold onto collect
struggle	try give up make peace

Practice 2. Complete each sentence, paying attention to the **bold** vocabulary word.

1. She did not like the book, **nor**

_____

2. **Unless** there is a change in the weather, we

_____

Practice 3. In your own words, explain why the boldfaced term in each sentence is used correctly or incorrectly.

1. The arrow hit **right square**, going past the target and into the trunk of a tree.

_____

_____

2. The man and his wife were **roomers**, living by themselves in a large house they owned in the suburbs.

_____

_____

3. If my dog does not learn to stop jumping up on people, I **have a great mind** to take him to obedience school.

_____

_____

Interpret the Text Using Close Reading

My Notes

Learning Target
● Apply understanding of how short stories are structured to comprehending the text.

Read and Annotate
Read "Thank You, M'am" and annotate the text as you read.

■ Use the My Notes area to write questions or ideas you have about the story.

■ Underline words and phrases that tell about the characters and setting.

■ Put a star next to the climax, or turning point, of the story.

■ Put exclamation marks next to the resolution of the story.

■ Circle any words or phrases that you do not understand.

Short Story

Thank You, M'am

by Langston Hughes

1   She was a large woman with a large purse that had everything in it but hammer and nails. It had a long strap, and she carried it slung across her shoulder. It was about eleven o'clock at night, and she was walking alone, when a boy ran up behind her and tried to snatch her purse.* The strap broke with the single tug the boy gave it from behind. But the boy's weight and the weight of the purse combined caused him to lose his balance so, instead of taking off full blast as he had hoped, the boy fell on his back on the sidewalk, and his legs flew up. The large woman simply turned around and kicked him right square in his blue-jeaned sitter. Then she reached down, picked the boy up by his shirt front, and shook him until his teeth rattled.

2   After that the woman said, "Pick up my pocketbook, boy, and give it here."

3   She still held him. But she bent down enough to permit him to **stoop** and pick up her purse. Then she said, "Now ain't you **ashamed** of yourself?"

4   Firmly gripped by his shirt front, the boy said, "Yes'm."

5   The woman said, "What did you want to do it for?"

6   The boy said, "I didn't aim to."

7   She said, "You a lie!"

8   By that time two or three people passed, stopped, turned to look, and some stood watching.

9   "If I turn you loose, will you run?" asked the woman.

10   "Yes'm," said the boy.

11   "Then I won't turn you loose," said the woman. She did not release him.

12   "I'm very sorry, lady, I'm sorry," whispered the boy.

13   "Um-hum! And your face is dirty. I got a great mind to wash your face for you. Ain't you got nobody home to tell you to wash your face?"

stoop: bend forward and down
ashame: feeling shame or guilt

14 "No'm," said the boy.

15 "Then it will get washed this evening," said the large woman starting up the street, dragging the frightened boy behind her.

16 He looked as if he were fourteen or fifteen, frail and **willow**-wild, in tennis shoes and blue jeans.

willow: long and thin, like a willow tree branch

17 The woman said, "You ought to be my son. I would teach you right from wrong. Least I can do right now is to wash your face. Are you hungry?"

18 "No'm," said the being-dragged boy. "I just want you to turn me loose."

19 "Was I bothering *you* when I turned that corner?" asked the woman.

20 "No'm."

21 "But you put yourself in contact with me," said the woman. "If you think that that contact is not going to last awhile, you got another thought coming. When I get through with you, sir, you are going to remember Mrs. Luella Bates Washington Jones."

22 Sweat popped out on the boy's face and he began to struggle. Mrs. Jones stopped, jerked him around in front of her, put a half-nelson about his neck, and continued to drag him up the street. When she got to her door, she dragged the boy inside, down a hall, and into a large kitchenette-furnished room at the rear of the house. She switched on the light and left the door open. The boy could hear other roomers laughing and talking in the large house. Some of their doors were open, too, so he knew he and the woman were not alone. The woman still had him by the neck in the middle of her room.

23 She said, "What is your name?"

24 "Roger," answered the boy.

25 "Then, Roger, you go to that sink and wash your face," said the woman, whereupon she turned him loose—at last. Roger looked at the door—looked at the woman—looked at the door—*and went to the sink.*

26 "Let the water run until it gets warm," she said. "Here's a clean towel."

27 "You gonna take me to jail?" asked the boy, bending over the sink.

28 "Not with that face, I would not take you nowhere," said the woman. "Here I am trying to get home to cook me a bite to eat and you snatch my pocketbook! Maybe, you ain't been to your supper either, late as it be. Have you?"

29 "There's nobody home at my house," said the boy.

30 "Then we'll eat," said the woman, "I believe you're hungry—or been hungry—to try to snatch my pocketbook."

31 "I wanted a pair of blue suede shoes," said the boy.

32 "Well, you didn't have to snatch my pocketbook to get some suede shoes," said Mrs. Luella Bates Washington Jones. "You could of asked me."

33 "M'am?"

34 The water dripping from his face, the boy looked at her. There was a long pause. A very long pause. After he had dried his face and not knowing what else to do, dried it again, the boy turned around, wondering what next. The door was open. He could make a dash for it down the hall. He could run, run, run, run, *run!*

My Notes

Interpret the Text Using Close Reading

My Notes

icebox: refrigerator

35 The woman was sitting on the day-bed. After a while she said, "I were young once and I wanted things I could not get."

36 There was another long pause. The boy's mouth opened. Then he frowned, but not knowing he frowned.

37 The woman said, "Um-hum! You thought I was going to say *but*, didn't you? You thought I was going to say, *but I didn't snatch people's pocketbooks.* Well, I wasn't going to say that." Pause. Silence. "I have done things, too, which I would not tell you, son—neither tell God, if he didn't already know. So you set down while I fix us something to eat. You might run that comb through your hair so you will look presentable.

38 In another corner of the room behind a screen was a gas plate and an **icebox**. Mrs. Jones got up and went behind the screen. The woman did not watch the boy to see if he was going to run now, nor did she watch her purse which she left behind her on the day-bed. But the boy took care to sit on the far side of the room where he thought she could easily see him out of the corner of her eye, if she wanted to. He did not trust the woman not to trust him. And he did not want to be mistrusted now.

39 "Do you need somebody to go to the store," asked the boy, "maybe to get some milk or something?"

40 "Don't believe I do," said the woman, "unless you just want sweet milk yourself. I was going to make cocoa out of this canned milk I got here."

41 "That will be fine," said the boy.

42 She heated some lima beans and ham she had in the icebox, made the cocoa, and set the table. The woman did not ask the boy anything about where he lived, or his folks, or anything else that would embarrass him. Instead, as they ate, she told him about her job in a hotel beauty-shop that stayed open late, what the work was like, and how all kinds of women came in and out, blondes, red-heads, and Spanish. Then she cut him a half of her ten-cent cake.

43 "Eat some more, son," she said.

44 When they were finished eating she got up and said, "Now, here, take this ten dollars and buy yourself some blue suede shoes. And next time, do not make the mistake of latching onto *my* pocketbook *nor nobody else's*—because shoes come by devilish like that will burn your feet. I got to get my rest now. But I wish you would behave yourself, son, from here on in."

45 She led him down the hall to the front door and opened it. "Goodnight! Behave yourself, boy!" she said, looking out into the street.

46 The boy wanted to say something else other than "Thank you, ma'am to Mrs. Luella Bates Washington Jones, but he couldn't do so as he turned at the barren stoop and looked back at the large woman in the door. He barely managed to say "Thank you" before she shut the door. And he never saw her again.

Interacting in Meaningful Ways: Academic Collaboration

Learning Targets

- Ask and answer questions about a short story in collaborative conversations, demonstrating active listening, and drawing upon an expanding pool of language resources for discussing literature.

- Express and support opinions of a short story in conversation.

Turn to your partner to discuss each question about "Thank You, M'am." After you have discussed a question, write notes about your answer before going on to the next question.

1. Who are the main characters in "Thank You, M'am"? What is their relationship like at first? How does it change during the course of the story?

> The main characters of the story are _____.

2. What is the conflict in the story? Is it an internal conflict or an external conflict? Cite evidence from the story that supports your conclusion.

> The text evidence shows that _____.

3. What is the theme of this story? What details from the text help you understand the theme?

> I think the theme is _____.

4. What inference can you make about Mrs. Luella Bates Washington Jones? Choose one or two phrases from the text that show what kind of person she is.

> The phrase _____ supports my inference because it shows _____.

Asking Questions

The resolution is the part of the story at which the conflict is solved or ended. With your partner or small group, read aloud paragraphs 44–46 of "Thank You, M'am." Discuss what questions you have about the resolution. Write one question to share with the whole class.

_____

_____

Interacting in Meaningful Ways: Analyze Sensory Language

WORD CONNECTIONS

Word Relationships

The adjective *vivid* means "producing clear, detailed images that seem like real life." Synonyms for *vivid* include *bright, lifelike, detailed,* and *striking*. Although these words are synonyms, each one has a slightly different meaning.

Language Resources

Vivid Verbs

Vague or weak verbs can leave a reader feeling bored and uninterested in a text. Vivid verbs describe the action in a story in clearer detail and add excitement. The following are two examples of ways to replace ordinary verbs with strong, vivid action words.

Run
scamper
dash
bolt
scramble

Talk
chatter
whisper
yell
murmur

Learning Target

● Analyze and explain in conversation and writing how sensory language such as vivid verbs produces effects on the reader.

The Opening of a Story

In the opening of a story, authors use words and phrases to introduce the reader to the characters and setting. The introduction can also be used to set up the conflict of a story. In the opening of "Thank You, M'am," the author, Langston Hughes, uses sensory language, such as vivid verbs, to heighten the action and set up the conflict of the story.

In this activity, you will look for language in the opening that sets up the story's conflict. As you read through paragraph 1 of "Thank You, M'am," write examples of vivid verbs in the chart. Then analyze each example to understand how this language helps set up the conflict in the story. Use a dictionary to look up the meaning of unfamiliar verbs.

Vivid Verb	Analyze the Effect
snatch	quick, sudden; builds drama, excitement

Quick Conversation

- Share your work with a partner. Read aloud your examples of vivid verbs, and take turns discussing your analysis. What effect does this language have on the reader? How does it set up the conflict in the story? Record notes from your discussion.

> I agree with _____ because _____.

> I think the verb _____ is effective because _____.

> Do you agree with my analysis?

Write a Short Argument

After citing examples of and analyzing vivid verbs in "Thank You, M'am," you have enough information to write a short argument. Choose one vivid verb from your chart. Write a short argument in which you explain the effect the language has on the reader. Give evidence of how it sets up the conflict of the story. Before writing, read the model short argument provided. Try structuring your argument in the same way.

_____

_____

_____

_____

MODEL: SHORT ARGUMENT
The author uses the verb "snatch" to explain how quickly and suddenly the boy tried to take the woman's purse. If the author had used a verb that was more vague, such as "take," the action would not have seemed as dramatic. Therefore, the vivid language helps set up the conflict of the story by heightening the action of Roger stealing Mrs. Jones's purse.

HEW How English Works: Story Structure

Learning Targets

- Apply basic understanding of how different text types are organized to express ideas to comprehending texts and writing basic texts.

- Students learn that in the *exposition*, words and phrases to orient the reader to the characters and setting are useful (e.g., *in a faraway land, one day in late summer, on the vast plains*).

- Students learn that in the *climax* and *rising action* stages, words and phrases for introducing conflicts or plot twists are useful (e.g., *unexpectedly, out of the blue, all of a sudden*).

Story Structure

Most stories follow the same basic structure. After the exposition, or opening, the story's rising action leads to a climax. Then, the falling action leads to the story's resolution, or ending. These five elements of plot help writers organize their ideas. The following chart tells more about story structure.

⚙ Language Resources: Story Structure

Exposition	the opening of a story; introduces the reader to the characters, setting, and the conflict
Rising Action	the main events that form the plot of a story; these events lead to the story's climax
Climax	the most exciting or important part of a story; the turning point
Falling Action	the events that lead to the ending of a story
Resolution	the point at the end of the story when the conflict is solved or ended

As you read "Thank You, M'am," look for sentences that illustrate each plot element in the Language Resources chart. Write in the following chart the paragraph(s) from the story that best illustrates each part of the story structure. Finally, write examples of words that the author uses to signal each of these elements.

Plot Element	Paragraph Number(s)	Examples from Text
exposition	paragraph 1	"She was a large woman" "eleven o'clock at night"
rising action		
climax		
falling action		
resolution		

Quick Conversation

- Share your work with a partner. Take turns sharing your examples from the text that show the stages of the story's structure. Compare and contrast your examples with those of your partner. Discuss how each element helps to organize the short story's plot. Record notes from your discussion.

> The reason I believe ____ is that ____.

> Will you please explain that?

> One difference between my example and yours is ____.

Write a Short Explanation

Using the knowledge you have gained in analyzing the structure of the story "Thank You, M'am," write a short explanation. Choose one of the stages of the story's plot and explain how the author used words and phrases to develop that element. Use the model short explanation to help you plan your writing.

_____

_____

_____

_____

MODEL: SHORT EXPLANATION
In the exposition, the author Langston Hughes uses words and phrases to orient the reader to the characters and setting of the story. Hughes uses words such as "large woman" to introduce the characters in the book. He describes the time of night and that "she was walking alone" to tell about the setting of the story.

Interacting in Meaningful Ways: Writing a Comparison

Language Resources

personal narrative: a story based on one's own life and told in the first-person point of view; follows incident-response-reflection structure

short story: a short work of fiction; plot structure includes rising action, climax, falling action, and resolution

Learning Target

● Write short informational texts collaboratively and independently.

● Apply basic understanding of how different text types are organized to express ideas to comprehending texts and writing basic texts.

Compare and contrast the main characteristics of personal narratives and short stories. Review your annotations and notes on "The Jacket" and "Thank You, M'am" and use them to complete the graphic organizer.

Word or Phrase	Personal Narrative	Short Story
definition		
point of view		
dialogue—the words characters say		
structure		

Quick Conversation

Share your work with your partner. Compare your ideas about the similarities and differences between personal narratives and short stories. How does the author use each text to express his or her ideas? Find examples from the texts to support your findings. Record notes from your discussion.

> One difference between personal narratives and short stories is _____.

> One similarity between personal narratives and short stories is _____.

> What evidence supports your thinking?

> Will you please repeat that?

Planning an Oral Presentation

Use the graphic organizer to plan an oral presentation in which you compare and contrast personal narratives and short stories.

Topic	Characteristics of Personal Narratives
Characteristics of Short Stories	**Visual Displays**

Expository Writing Prompt

Write a draft of your oral presentation. Be sure to:

- ◼ Develop a topic with relevant facts, definitions, and concrete details.
- ◼ Include precise language and vocabulary that describes each type of text.
- ◼ Plan any visual displays to clarify information.
- ◼ End the presentation by stating your opinion on which text type you prefer and why.

_____

_____

_____

_____

_____

_____

_____

_____

_____

_____

_____

_____

_____

_____

Selecting Language Resources

Learning Targets

● Develop language resources to use in one's speaking and writing about short stories.

● Use an expanded set of words to create precision while speaking and writing.

● Adjust language choices to suit the academic setting.

The chart presents words and phrases you will use in discussion and writing. Think about each word or phrase. Circle Q, H, or T to indicate how well you know it. Work with a partner, asking your partner to explain each word or phrase. Listen closely to the explanation, and then write your partner's name and condensed idea in the In Our Own Words column.

Rating	Q	H	T
	I have seen this word or phrase, but I have **questions** about its meaning.	I have **heard** this word or phrase, but do not know it well.	I know this word or phrase so well that I could **teach** it to someone else.

Word or Phrase	Definition	In Our Own Words
characterization Rating Q H T	the way a writer describes the character or qualities of a person or thing	
setting Rating Q H T	the time and place in which a story takes place	
dialogue Rating Q H T	the words that characters say in a story	
repetition Rating Q H T	in literature, something that is written over and over again	
sensory language Rating Q H T	the use of details to add color and depth to writing; uses details from the five senses (sight, touch, hearing, taste, smell)	
theme Rating Q H T	the central idea, message, or purpose of a literary work	

Academic and Social Language Preview

Learning Target

- Develop knowledge of a growing set of academic and social vocabulary to use in reading, speaking, and writing.

VOCABULARY PREVIEW

germ: (noun) a very small living thing that causes illness

invisible: (adjective) not visible, impossible to see

period: (noun) one of the parts that the school day is divided into

plastic: (noun) a strong, light material that can be made into different shapes and that is used to make many common products

pretend: (verb) to act like something is true when it is not

rattle: (verb) to move or shake and make a loud noise

underneath: (preposition) below or beneath something

wear: (verb) to use as clothing

Vocabulary Practice

Use the definitions in the Vocabulary Preview or a dictionary to support your work.

Practice 1. Draw a line to match each vocabulary word to the word closest in meaning.

rattle	make believe
period	class
pretend	clink

Practice 2. Complete the paragraph with the correct vocabulary words from the list.

I wanted to _____ my favorite sweater to the dance on Friday night. But I couldn't

find it anywhere. It seemed to be _____! Finally, I spied it _____

a pile of books in the corner of my room.

Practice 3. For each word, write a definition in your own words. Include examples that will help a reader understand the word better.

1. **germ:**

   _____

   _____

2. **plastic:**

   _____

   _____

Interpret the Text Using Close Reading

Learning Target
- Apply understanding of how short stories are structured to comprehending the text.

Read and Annotate
Read "Eleven" and annotate the text as you read.
- ■ Use the My Notes area to write questions or ideas you have about the story.
- ■ Underline examples of repetition.
- ■ Put a star next to the conflicts that occur in the short story.
- ■ Circle unknown words and phrases.

Short Story

Eleven

from *Woman Hollering Creek and Other Stories,* by Sandra Cisneros

1   What they don't understand about birthdays and what they never tell you is that when you're eleven, you're also ten, and nine, and eight, and seven, and six, and five, and four, and three, and two, and one. And when you wake up on your eleventh birthday you expect to feel eleven, but you don't. You open your eyes and everything's just like yesterday, only it's today. And you don't feel eleven at all. You feel like you're still ten. And you are—underneath the year that makes you eleven.

2   Like some days you might say something stupid, and that's the part of you that's still ten. Or maybe some days you might need to sit on your mama's lap because you're scared, and that's the part of you that's five. And maybe one day when you're all grown up maybe you will need to cry like if you're three, and that's okay. That's what I tell Mama when she's sad and needs to cry. Maybe she's feeling three.

3   Because the way you grow old is kind of like an onion or like the rings inside a tree trunk or like my little wooden dolls that fit one inside the other, each year inside the next one. That's how being eleven years old is.

4   You don't feel eleven. Not right away. It takes a few days, weeks even, sometimes even months before you say Eleven when they ask you. And you don't feel smart eleven, not until you're almost twelve. That's the way it is.

5   Only today I wish I didn't have only eleven years rattling inside me like pennies in a tin Band-Aid box. Today I wish I was one hundred and two instead of eleven because if I was one hundred and two I'd have known what to say when Mrs. Price put the red sweater on my desk. I would've known how to tell her it wasn't mine instead of just sitting there with that look on my face and nothing coming out of my mouth.

6   "Whose is this?" Mrs. Price says, and she holds the red sweater up in the air for all the class to see. "Whose? It's been sitting in the coatroom for a month."

7   "Not mine," says everybody. "Not me."

My Notes

Interpret the Text Using Close Reading

My Notes

raggedy: in poor condition; worn, tattered

parking meter: machine next to a street into which people pay for a parking space

hiccup: a sound in the throat that comes from uncontrolled muscle movements in the chest

8 "It has to belong to somebody," Mrs. Price keeps saying, but nobody can remember. It's an ugly sweater with red plastic buttons and a collar and sleeves all stretched out like you could use it for a jump rope. It's maybe a thousand years old and even if it belonged to me I wouldn't say so.

9 Maybe because I'm skinny, maybe because she doesn't like me, that stupid Sylvia Saldívar says, "I think it belongs to Rachel." An ugly sweater like that, all **raggedy** and old, but Mrs. Price believes her. Mrs. Price takes the sweater and puts it right on my desk, but when I open my mouth nothing comes out.

10 "That's not, I don't, you're not . . . Not mine," I finally say in a little voice that was maybe me when I was four.

11 "Of course it's yours," Mrs. Price says. "I remember you wearing it once." Because she's older and the teacher, she's right and I'm not.

12 Not mine, not mine, not mine, but Mrs. Price is already turning to page thirty-two, and math problem number four. I don't know why but all of a sudden I'm feeling sick inside, like the part of me that's three wants to come out of my eyes, only I squeeze them shut tight and bite down on my teeth real hard and try to remember today I am eleven, eleven. Mama is making a cake for me for tonight, and when Papa comes home everybody will sing Happy birthday, happy birthday to you.

13 But when the sick feeling goes away and I open my eyes, the red sweater's still sitting there like a big red mountain. I move the red sweater to the corner of my desk with my ruler. I move my pencil and books and eraser as far from it as possible. I even move my chair a little to the right. Not mine, not mine, not mine.

14 In my head I'm thinking how long till lunchtime, how long till I can take the red sweater and throw it over the schoolyard fence, or leave it hanging on a **parking meter**, or bunch it up into a little ball and toss it in the alley. Except when math period ends, Mrs. Price says loud and in front of everybody, "Now, Rachel, that's enough," because she sees I've shoved the red sweater to the tippy-tip corner of my desk and it's hanging all over the edge like a waterfall, but I don't care.

15 "Rachel," Mrs. Price says. She says it like she's getting mad. "You put that sweater on right now and no more nonsense."

16 "But it's not—"

17 "Now!" Mrs. Price says.

18 This is when I wish I wasn't eleven, because all the years inside of me—ten, nine, eight, seven, six, five, four, three, two, and one—are pushing at the back of my eyes when I put one arm through one sleeve of the sweater that smells like cottage cheese, and then the other arm through the other and stand there with my arms apart like if the sweater hurts me and it does, all itchy and full of germs that aren't even mine.

19 That's when everything I've been holding in since this morning, since when Mrs. Price put the sweater on my desk, finally lets go, and all of a sudden I'm crying in front of everybody. I wish I was invisible but I'm not. I'm eleven and it's my birthday today and I'm crying like I'm three in front of everybody. I put my head down on the desk and bury my face in my stupid clown-sweater arms. My face all hot and spit coming out of my mouth because I can't stop the little animal noises from coming out of me, until there aren't any more tears left in my eyes, and it's just my body shaking like when you have the **hiccups**, and my whole head hurts like when you drink milk too fast.

Interpret the Text Using Close Reading

20 But the worst part is right before the bell rings for lunch. That stupid Phyllis Lopez, who is even dumber than Sylvia Saldívar, says she remembers the red sweater is hers! I take it off right away and give it to her, only Mrs. Price pretends like everything's okay.

21 Today I'm eleven. There's a cake Mama's making for tonight, and when Papa comes home from work we'll eat it. There'll be candles and presents, and everybody will sing Happy birthday, happy birthday to you, Rachel, only it's too late.

22 I'm eleven today. I'm eleven, ten, nine, eight, seven, six, five, four, three, two, and one, but I wish I was one hundred and two. I wish I was anything but eleven, because I want today to be far away already, far away like a runaway balloon, like a tiny o in the sky, so tiny-tiny you have to close your eyes to see it.

My Notes

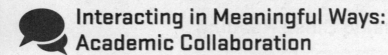

Interacting in Meaningful Ways: Academic Collaboration

Learning Targets

- Ask and answer questions about a short story in collaborative conversations, demonstrating active listening, and drawing upon an expanding pool of language resources for discussing literature.

- Express and support opinions of a short story in conversation.

Turn to your partner or small group to discuss each question about "Eleven." After you have discussed a question, write notes about your answer before going on to the next question.

1. What is the main conflict that occurs in the story?

> I think the main conflict of the story is ____.

2. Read the dialogue between Mrs. Price and Rachel in paragraphs 10–11 and 14–17. What inference can the reader make about Mrs. Price based on this dialogue?

> Based on ____ the reader can infer ____.

3. Who is Phyllis Lopez? What can the reader infer about her character from her actions near the end of the story?

> The reader can infer that ____.

4. What evidence from the story shows that Rachel experienced both external and internal conflicts?

> The text evidence ____ shows that ____.

Asking Questions

With your partner or small group, read aloud paragraph 19 of "Eleven." Discuss what questions you have about the climax. Write one question to share with the whole class.

_____

_____

Learning Target

- Analyze and explain in conversation how figurative language used in a short story produces effects on the reader.

Figurative Language

Figurative language is language that writers use to move beyond the literal meaning of a word or phrase. Figurative language can enhance a story's descriptions and produce different effects on the reader. In "Eleven," the author, Sandra Cisneros, uses figurative language to add interest and special effects to her writing.

 Language Resources: Figurative Language

Figure of Speech	Definition	Example
personification	the act of giving human qualities to non-human things	***The clouds danced*** *across the sky.*
metaphor	a way of describing something by comparing it to something else	*The doghouse is buried under a* ***blanket*** *of snow.*
simile	a phrase that describes something by comparing it to something else; often uses the word "like" or "as"	*After school, she felt* ***free as a bird***. *I* ***ran like the wind*** *to catch the bus.*

As you read through "Eleven," look for examples of figurative language. Write three examples of figurative language from the text in the chart, including which figure of speech is being used. Then analyze each example to understand the effect the author is trying to create. Use the Language Resources: Figurative Language chart for support.

Example from Text	Analyze the Effect	Evaluate How Effective It Is
simile: "the way you grow old is kind of like an onion"	The layers of an onion fit together. Rachel thinks when you grow old, you can feel each passing year inside yourself.	

 **Quick Conversation**

● Share your work with a partner. Read aloud your examples of figurative language. Take turns explaining your analysis and evaluation of each example. Discuss whether your partner agrees or disagrees with your evaluation. Record notes from your discussion.

> In my opinion, this simile means ____.

> Do you agree with my analysis?

> One example of personification is ____.

> I agree/disagree with your evaluation because ____.

Write a Short Description

After finding and analyzing examples of figurative language in "Eleven," you can come up with new examples in your own writing. Write a fictional description of Rachel's twelfth birthday celebration. Decide if it is better or worse than her eleventh birthday, and use figurative language to create that effect. Use a table to plan the figurative language in your description. In addition, refer to the model short description.

_____

_____

_____

_____

MODEL: SHORT DESCRIPTION

Rachel hurries home from school. Her legs feel light as air. She doesn't want to be late for her birthday party. Rachel is turning twelve and it feels like the whole town is ready to celebrate. When she finally reaches her house, it stands proud, welcoming her with open arms. Inside, her family stands in the kitchen, a cake like a beautifully wrapped present sitting on the kitchen table.

Learning Target

- Apply basic understanding of how different text types are organized to express ideas when comprehending texts and writing basic texts.

Recognizing Conflicts

The conflict or conflicts that occur are a central part of any story. They can be both internal and external. Writers use conflicts to advance other elements of the plot, such as the story's rising action, climax, and resolution.

In the following plot diagram, some of the boxes have been filled in for you. Label the diagram with the conflicts that occur in "Eleven." Include both internal and external conflicts. Use the Language Resources box to help you.

WORD CONNECTIONS

Multiple-Meaning Words

The word *advance* can have multiple meanings. In this paragraph, it is a verb meaning "to move forward." In other contexts, it can be an adjective or a noun. The phrase *in advance* means "before something happens."

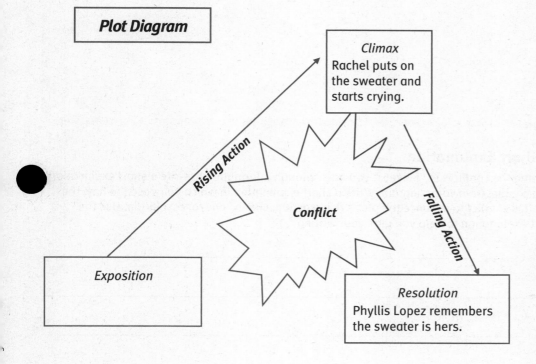

Plot Diagram

Climax
Rachel puts on the sweater and starts crying.

Rising Action

Conflict

Falling Action

Exposition

Resolution
Phyllis Lopez remembers the sweater is hers.

Language Resources

Internal Conflict: a conflict in which the character struggles with something inside himself or herself, such as the character's desires or emotions

External Conflict: a conflict in which the character struggles with an outside force, such as another person or something in nature

Rising Action: the main events that form the plot of a story; these events lead to the story's climax

Climax: the most exciting or important part of a story; the turning point

Resolution: the point at the end of the story when the conflict is solved or ended

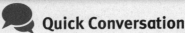 **Quick Conversation**

- Share your work with a partner. Read aloud the conflicts you entered in the chart, and discuss how they compare. Then read aloud the rest of the information that was provided in the chart. How does each conflict advance the story's rising action, climax, and resolution? Record notes from your discussion.

> In my opinion, _____.

> One difference between my example and yours is _____.

> One conflict from the story is _____.

> Will you please explain that?

Write a Short Explanation

After analyzing the conflicts in "Eleven," you have enough information to write a short explanation. Choose one conflict from your diagram. Write a short explanation in which you describe how the writer uses this conflict to advance the plot's rising action, climax, and/or resolution. Use the model short explanation to help you plan your writing.

_____

_____

_____

_____

MODEL: SHORT EXPLANATION

One conflict in "Eleven" is the external conflict between Rachel and Mrs. Price. Rachel does not want to put on the ugly red sweater, and Mrs. Price keeps telling her to put it on. This conflict advances the plot of the story. Their interaction leads to the climax, when Rachel starts crying. Eventually, the conflict is ended in the resolution.

Personal Narrative
Narrative Writing

Step 1: Introduction

In this unit, you have read three narratives that all told the stories of young people who experience a struggle while growing up. Now you will be writing your own personal narrative similar to others you have read in this unit. Think about the personal experiences the writers shared in "The Jacket," "Thank You, M'am," and "Eleven."

Narrative Writing Prompt

You will write a personal narrative about an incident that was difficult for you but which caused you to grow. Be sure to

- Establish the incident (setting, conflict, character).

- Describe the response (feelings and actions).

- Write from the first-person point of view and include details about the narrator's and other characters' feelings.

- Use figurative language such as similes and metaphors to let readers know how the narrator feels.

- End your story by reflecting how the narrator grew or learned from the incident.

Step 2: Brainstorming

Now you are ready to start thinking about what you will write about. Work in small groups or with a partner to brainstorm ideas using the following graphic organizer.

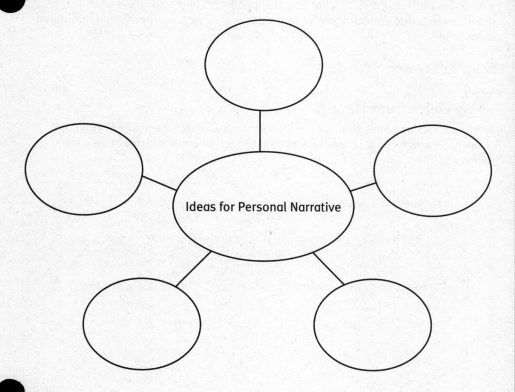

Ideas for Personal Narrative

Personal Narrative
Narrative Writing

My Notes

 Quick Conversation

Discuss the ideas that you brainstormed with your partner or group. Use the following sentence frames to help you in your discussion. Remember to take turns sharing your ideas. Ask each other questions. After your discussion, draw a star next to the idea that you choose to write about.

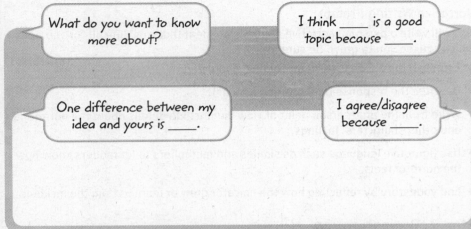

What do you want to know more about?

I think _____ is a good topic because _____.

One difference between my idea and yours is _____.

I agree/disagree because _____.

Quickwrite: Next, complete a Quickwrite about the topic you have chosen. Include a brief description of the incident you struggled with and what you learned as a result. Read aloud your Quickwrite to a partner. Ask your partner to add additional ideas in writing.

Step 3: Prewriting

 Quick Conversation

Share your ideas about your topic with a partner. Discuss the incident you have chosen, as well as your response and your reflection on that incident. Ask for feedback.

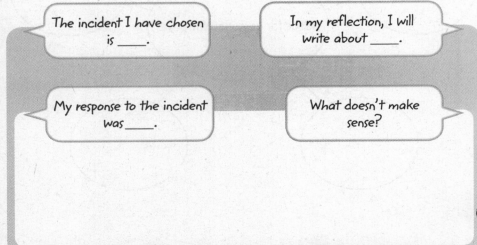

The incident I have chosen is _____.

In my reflection, I will write about _____.

My response to the incident was _____.

What doesn't make sense?

Personal Narrative
Narrative Writing

Record notes from your discussion. Use the graphic organizer to make a plan for your personal narrative.

Incident	Response	Reflection
What is the central action that is the focus of your story?	**How did you feel and what did you do as a result of the incident?**	**What was the significance of the incident? How did you learn or grow from it?**

Step 4: Drafting

Use your completed graphic organizer and brainstorming word web to help you as you begin to draft your personal narrative. Before you begin your draft, review the Scoring Guide on page 44–45 so that you understand how your narrative will be assessed.

Remember what you have learned in this unit to make your writing stronger and more interesting. Fill in the following graphic organizer to help you add figurative language and vivid verbs to your draft. Write at least one example of figurative language and a vivid verb that you can add to each part of your narrative.

	Figurative Language (similes, metaphors, personification)	**Vivid Verbs**
Incident		
Response		
Reflection		

Be sure your draft includes:

- a clear description of the incident (setting, conflict, character), as well as the narrator's response to the incident
- figurative language such as similes, metaphors, and personification
- vivid verbs
- dialogue to develop the characters and the incident
- correct use of grammar and punctuation
- a reflection at the end of the narrative describing what the narrator learned

Language Resources

Vivid Verbs

You can replace vague or weak verbs with strong, vivid verbs that bring the action to life for your readers. Here are some common verbs with ideas for synonyms that are more vivid and precise.

Vivid Verbs

Instead of . . .	Try using . . .
walk	amble, hike, lumber, ramble, saunter, stride, stroll, trudge
speak	bellow, chuckle, hiss, holler, laugh, mumble, scream, shout, sigh, warn, whimper, whisper
do	achieve, complete, compose, construct, create, perform, produce
see	detect, discern, distinguish, examine, notice, observe, perceive, witness, glimpse, spy

Personal Narrative
Narrative Writing

Writing Checklist

- [ ] Review the Narrative Writing Rubric.
- [ ] Review the Student Narrative Writing Exemplar.
- [ ] Review your draft.
- [ ] Participate in peer editing.
- [ ] Revise.
- [ ] Publish.
- [ ] Present.

My Notes

Step 5: Editing and Revising

With a partner, review the Scoring Guide found at the end of this assessment again. Then look at the Student Narrative Text Exemplar, which you will receive from your teacher. Exchange drafts with your partner. Read each other's drafts. Use the Peer Editing Checklist as you review your partner's draft.

Peer Editing Checklist

- [ ] Did the writer follow the prompt?
- [ ] Did the writer include an incident, response, and reflection?
- [ ] Is the writing organized in a way that makes sense?
- [ ] Did the writer vary sentence structures to make the writing more interesting?
- [ ] Did the writer include transitions to add details about the central idea and connect supporting paragraphs?
- [ ] Did the writer include vivid verbs and figurative language?
- [ ] Are there any spelling or punctuation mistakes?
- [ ] Are there any grammar errors?

💬 Quick Conversation

With your partner, discuss each other's drafts. Give feedback to help improve each other's writing. Record notes from your discussion.

> I liked your use of the verb _____ because _____.

> The organization here needs improvement because _____.

> I was confused when _____.

> I think you followed the prompt well because _____.

Look at the Peer Editing Checklist that your partner completed. Use it to help you revise your draft. Then use a classroom computer to revise and complete your draft. You may include graphics or images from the Internet to include in your final draft, but make sure they are appropriate. Check your final narrative against the Scoring Guide before you submit it to your teacher.

Personal Narrative
Narrative Writing

Step 6: Sharing

Present your personal narrative orally. You may use visual aids to help you. Keep the following points in mind both as you are presenting and while you are listening to your classmates' presentations.

Tips for Presenting	Tips for Listening
Keep these points in mind as you are presenting: • Speak loudly and clearly. • Maintain eye contact with your audience. • Listen respectfully to any questions from your audience. • Respond thoughtfully to any questions from your audience.	As your classmates present, be an active listener: • Take notes. • Listen for the speaker's purpose and main point. • Listen for the *who? what? where? when? how? why?* • Jot down any questions you may have for the presenter.

Complete the Active Listening graphic organizer after you listen to each presenter.

Content

The presenter's purpose was to _____.

The presenter's main point was _____.

I agree/disagree with the presenter because _____.

Form

☐ The presenter did/did not use a clear, loud voice.

☐ The presenter did/did not make eye contact.

One thing the presenter could improve is _____.

Feedback

One thing I really liked about the presentation was _____.

A question I still have is _____.

Step 7: Feedback

Now that you have received feedback on your work, note what you did well and what still needs improvement.

What Went Well	What Needs Improvement

Personal Narrative
Narrative Writing

SCORING GUIDE

Scoring Criteria	4	3	2	1
Ideas	The narrative • presents a clearly focused and significant incident • develops experiences, events, and/or characters through thorough and effective use of dialogue and descriptive details.	The narrative • presents a focused and significant incident • develops experiences, events, and/or characters through techniques such as dialogue and descriptive details.	The narrative • presents an inconsistently focused incident • begins to develop experiences, events, and/or characters through some use of dialogue and/or descriptive details.	The narrative • presents an unfocused or unclear incident • fails to develop experiences, events, and/or characters; minimal use of elaborative techniques.
Structure	The narrative • engages and orients the reader in an introduction • sequences events in the incident and response logically and naturally • uses a variety of transitions effectively • provides an insightful reflective conclusion.	The narrative • orients the reader with an adequate introduction • sequences events in the incident and response logically • uses transitional words, phrases, and clauses to link events and signal shifts • provides a reflective conclusion.	The narrative • provides a weak or unrelated introduction • sequences events unevenly • uses inconsistent, repetitive, or basic transitional words, phrases, and clauses • provides a weak or disconnected conclusion.	The narrative • lacks an introduction • sequences events illogically • uses few or no transitions • lacks a conclusion.
Use of Language	The narrative • uses precise words and sensory language effectively to convey the experience • demonstrates command of the conventions of standard English capitalization, punctuation, spelling, grammar, and usage (including pronoun use, sentence variety, dialogue, and punctuation).	The narrative • uses generally precise words and sensory language to convey the experience • demonstrates adequate command of the conventions of standard English capitalization, punctuation, spelling, grammar, and usage (including pronoun use, sentence variety, dialogue, and punctuation).	The narrative • uses few precise words and little sensory language • demonstrates partial or inconsistent command of the conventions of standard English capitalization, punctuation, spelling, grammar, and usage (including pronoun use, sentence variety, dialogue, and punctuation).	The narrative • uses limited, vague, and unclear words and language • lacks command of the conventions of standard English capitalization, punctuation, spelling, grammar, and usage; frequent errors obscure meaning.
Collaboration	Student exceeds expectations in working collaboratively with others.	Student works collaboratively with others.	Student needs development in working collaboratively with others.	Student does not work collaboratively with others.

Scoring Criteria	4	3	2	1
How English Works	The narrative • uses vivid verbs consistently to help the reader visualize details • uses first- and third-person pronouns correctly and effectively.	The narrative • uses vivid verbs that help the reader visualize details • uses first- and third-person pronouns correctly.	The narrative • uses weak vivid verbs and/or uses them inconsistently • uses some pronouns correctly.	The narrative • lacks the use of vivid verbs to help the reader visualize details • uses first- and/or third-person pronouns incorrectly.
Interact in Meaningful Ways	The narrative • uses a variety of strong figurative language such as similes and metaphors to produce different effects on the reader • develops both internal and external conflicts that advance the plot.	The narrative • uses some figurative language such as similes and metaphors to produce different effects on the reader • develops a conflict that advances the plot.	The narrative • uses ineffective or weak figurative language • develops a weak conflict that does not advance the plot.	The narrative • lacks figurative language • lacks any conflicts.

Reflections

Use this space to write a reflection about what you learned in this unit.

UNIT
2

THE POWER TO CHANGE:
Analyzing Literature and Creating Expository Text

Visual Prompt: Plants change from one season to another and often grow in unexpected places. What trait would this plant show that you might use in your own goals for change?

Unit Overview

In this unit, you will read an excerpt from the novel *Walk Two Moons* and compare and contrast its characters. You will take a trip with John Steinbeck and his dog Charley to Yellowstone National Park and learn about how dogs affect the lives of humans in Temple Grandin's autobiography. Finally, you will reflect on the techniques that authors use to explain their ideas and apply them to your own expository writing.

ACTIVITY
1.1

Selecting Language Resources

WORD
CONNECTIONS

Roots

The root word *litera* in *literary* means "letters." This root word can also been seen in the word *literature*, which is a written work such as a book. *Literary* means "used in literature."

Learning Targets

- Develop language resources to use in one's speaking and writing about narrative elements.

- Use an expanded set of words to create precision while speaking and writing.

- Adjust language choices to suit the academic setting.

The chart presents words and phrases you will use in discussion and writing. Think about each word or phrase. Circle Q, H, or T to indicate how well you know it. Work with a partner, asking your partner to explain each word or phrase. Listen closely to the explanation, and then write your partner's name in the In Our Own Words column along with his or her condensed idea.

Rating	Q	H	T
	I have seen this word or phrase, but I have **questions** about its meaning.	I have **heard** this word or phrase, but do not know it well.	I know this word or phrase so well that I could **teach** it to someone else.

Word or Phrase	Definition	In Our Own Words
fiction Rating Q H T	a story about a person or event that is not true or is imagined	
novel Rating Q H T	a story that is often long and about a character or event that is not true or imagined	
character Rating Q H T	a person or animal in a story	
trait Rating Q H T	a quality or characteristic that makes a character unique or different	
topic sentence Rating Q H T	a sentence that expresses the key thought or idea of a paragraph or written piece of work	
commentary Rating Q H T	a discussion in which people write or share orally their opinion about someone or something	
characterization Rating Q H T	the methods a writer uses to develop characters, for example, through description, actions, and dialogue	

Academic and Social Language Preview

Learning Target
- Develop knowledge of a growing set of academic and social vocabulary to use in reading, speaking, and writing.

VOCABULARY PREVIEW

brave: (adjective) fearless or not afraid

courageous: (adjective) brave or showing courage

dignified: (adjective) formal or showing respect

enormous: (adjective) a very large size or amount

huge: (adjective) very large

investigating: (verb) trying to find out about something such as to learn facts about how something happened

lunatic: (noun) someone who is crazy or insane

moody: (adjective) having many different moods that change often

out of the blue: (idiom) unexpectedly

parched: (adjective) dry or really thirsty

peculiar: (adjective) strange or not normal

singlehandedly: (adjective) done without help from anyone else

terrified: (adjective) very afraid or frightened

Vocabulary Practice

Use the definitions in the Vocabulary Preview or a dictionary to support your work.

Practice 1. Draw lines between the words that are synonyms and cross out the words that remain.

dignified	peculiar
huge	courageous
investigating	moody
brave	enormous

Practice 2. Complete each sentence, paying attention to the **bold** vocabulary word.

1. Walking in the desert made them **parched**, so they

_____

2. The **lunatic** who crashed into their car **terrified** them because

_____

3. The police were **investigating** the robbery to

_____

Practice 3. Choose the best word to complete each sentence.

1. He was a _____ person, with respectful and elegant manners. (courageous, dignified)
2. There is something very _____ about the way she stares at everyone in the room. (terrified, peculiar)
3. The detective was _____ the theft of our neighbor's car. (investigating, peculiar)

Practice 4. The English language has many words and phrases that have both **literal** and **figurative** meanings. The **literal** meaning of a word is the ordinary or usual meaning of the word. For example, the literal meaning of the phrase "know the ropes" is to know a lot about ropes. The **figurative** meaning of a word expresses an idea in an interesting way by using language that usually describes something else. For example, the figurative meaning of "know the ropes" is to know a lot about how to do something, not literally ropes. Look at the following phrases from *Walk Two Moons* and record both their literal and figurative meanings.

Word/Phrase	Literal Meaning	Figurative Meaning
singlehandedly		
out of the blue		

Language Resources

You may already know that **antonyms** are words that have opposite meanings, while **synonyms** are words that mean the same thing. If you say that something is **synonymous**, you are saying that it means the same thing. For instance, "Some people say that good sleeping habits are synonymous with good health."

Interpret the Text Using Close Reading

Learning Target
● Read closely to explain the similarities and differences between characters.

Read and Annotate
Read the excerpt from *Walk Two Moons* and annotate the text as you read.
■ Use the My Notes area to write questions or ideas you have about the story.
■ Underline words and phrases that people use to describe Sal.
■ Put a star next to the event that shows Sal is brave.
■ Place an exclamation mark next to a surprising realization Sal has.
■ Circle unknown words.

© 2017 College Board. All rights reserved.

Novel
excerpt from
Walk Two Moons

by Sharon Creech

Salamanca "Sal" Hiddle and her grandparents are on a cross-country trip to Idaho to see Sal's mother. While they are on the road, Sal entertains her grandparents by telling them the "extensively strange story" of her friend Phoebe Winterbottom. The following excerpt describes Sal and Phoebe's first face-to-face encounter.

1 Three days later, I started school and saw Phoebe again. She was in my class. Most of the kids in my new school spoke in quick, sharp bursts and dressed in stiff, new clothes and wore braces on their teeth. Most girls wore their hair in exactly the same way: in a shoulder-length bob (that's what they called it) with long bangs that they repeatedly shook out of their eyes. We once had a horse who did that.

2 Everybody kept touching my hair. "Don't you ever cut it?" they said. "Can you sit on it? How do you wash it? Is it naturally black like that? Do you use conditioner?" I couldn't tell if they liked my hair or if they thought I looked like a **whang-doodle**.

3 One girl, Mary Lou Finney, said the most peculiar things, like out of the blue she would say, "**Omnipotent**!" or "Beef brain!" I couldn't make any sense of it. There were Megan and Christy, who jumped up and down like parched peas, moody Beth Ann, and pink-cheeked Alex. There was Ben, who drew cartoons all day long, and a peculiar English teacher named Mr. Birkway.

4 And then there was Phoebe Winterbottom. Ben called her "Free Bee Ice Bottom" and drew a picture of a bumblebee with an ice cube on its bottom. Phoebe tore it up.

5 Phoebe was a quiet girl who stayed mostly by herself. She had a pleasant round face and huge, enormous sky-blue eyes. Around this pleasant round face, her hair—as yellow as a crow's foot—curled in short ringlets.

My Notes

Why do the other students keep touching Sal's hair?

whang-doodle: a made-up creature

omnipotent: all powerful

My Notes

Alpha and Omega: the beginning and the end

6 During that first week, when my father and I were at Margaret's (we ate dinner there three times that week), I saw Phoebe's face twice more at her window. Once I waved at her, but she didn't seem to notice, and at school she never mentioned that she had seen me.

7 Then one day at lunch, she slid into the seat next to me and said, "Sal, you're so courageous. You're ever so brave."

8 To tell you the truth, I was surprised. You could have knocked me over with a chicken feather. "Me? I'm not brave," I said.

9 "You are. You are brave."

10 I was not. I, Salamanca Tree Hiddle, was afraid of lots and lots of things. For example, I was terrified of car accidents, death, cancer, brain tumors, nuclear war, pregnant women, loud noises, strict teachers, elevators, and scads of other things. But I was not afraid of spiders, snakes, and wasps. Phoebe, and nearly everyone else in my new class, did not have much fondness for these creatures.

11 But on that day, when a dignified black spider was investigating my desk, I cupped my hands around it, carried it to the open window, and set it outside on the ledge. Mary Lou Finney said, "**Alpha and Omega**, will you look at that!" Beth Ann was as white as milk. All around the room, people were acting as if I had singlehandedly taken on a fire-breathing dragon.

12 What I have since realized is that if people expect you to be brave, sometimes you pretend that you are, even when you are frightened down to your very bones. / But this was later, during the whole thing with Phoebe's lunatic, that I realized 'this.

13 At this point in my story, Gram interrupted me to say, "Why, Salamanca, of course you're brave. All the Hiddles are brave. It's a family trait. Look at your daddy—your momma—"

Interacting in Meaningful Ways: Academic Collaboration

Learning Targets

- Ask and answer questions about the characters in the novel in collaborative conversations, demonstrating active listening, and drawing upon an expanding pool of language resources for discussing literature.

- Express and support opinions of a narrative in conversation.

- Read closely to make inferences and draw conclusions.

Turn to your partner or small group to discuss each question about *Walk Two Moons*. After you have discussed a question, write notes about your answer before going on to the next question.

1. What evidence from this story shows that Phoebe thinks Sal is brave?

> The text evidence _____ shows that _____.

2. Which phrase in this story gives the reader insight into the kind of person Phoebe is?

> I think the phrase _____ is effective because _____.

3. What inference can you make about Sal?

> Based on _____, I think _____.

4. In paragraph 12, what words in this story does the author use to describe Sal? How do these words help you understand Sal's character?

> The words _____ are effective because _____.

Asking Questions

With your partner or small group, read aloud the ending of *Walk Two Moons* excerpt, paragraphs 11 and 12. Discuss what questions you have about Sal. Write one question to share with the whole class.

_____

_____

HEW

How English Works:
Adjectives and Adjectival Phrases

Learning Target
- Explain how well the author uses language to develop the characters in a novel.

Adjectives and Adjectival Phrases

Walk Two Moons is a novel written in the first-person point of view. The narrator is a character in the story, telling about her journey and encounters with other characters as she searches for her mother. The author uses descriptive words and phrases to reveal characters' thoughts, feelings, and traits.

An adjective is a word that modifies a noun or pronoun.
> The sky is **blue**.

In this example, *blue* is the adjective that modifies the noun *sky*.

An adjectival phrase is a group of words that function as an adjective.
> The book **on the shelf** is the one **to read** if you are working on the report.

The adjectival phrases *one the shelf* and *to read* both modify the noun *book*.

⚙ Language Resources: Adjectives and Adjectival Phrases

Adjectives	brave	courageous	shy	loud	timid	reluctant
Adjectival Phrases	white as milk	stiff, new clothes	cold, icy winter	shiny, blond hair	bright blue eyes	strong as an ox

Skim through *Walk Two Moons*, looking for sentences you like that have adjectives or adjectival phrases. Write three examples of each in the chart. Use the Language Resources: Adjectives and Adjectival Phrases chart for support.

Examples of Adjectives from *Walk Two Moons*	Examples of Adjectival Phrases from *Walk Two Moons*
quiet	yellow as a crow's foot

Quick Conversation

- Share your work with a partner. Read aloud the examples you wrote. Discuss how they compare.
- What is the effect of using adjectives and adjectival phrases in the development of character traits? Record notes from your discussion.

> I think that _____ is a strong (adjective/adjectival phrase) to describe (Phoebe/Sal) because _____.

> One difference between my examples and yours is _____.

> I like the adjectival phrase _____ because _____.

Oral Presentation of a Short Argument

In a brief oral presentation, share what you learned from your discussion and the activity on the use of adjectives and adjectival phrases in the development of characterization. Include details and specific examples from the novel to support your argument. Use the space below to prepare your short oral presentation.

_____

_____

_____

_____

How English Works:
Transitions for Comparison and Contrast

 Language Resources
Compare: to show how two or more things are alike or similar
Compound Sentence: a sentence that has two independent clauses joined by a connecting word such as *and, but,* or *so.*
Contrast: to show how two or more things are different or opposite

ACADEMIC VOCABULARY
Analyze is a verb that means to study or look at something carefully and closely. When you **analyze** text, you create an **analysis** of it. It shows that you have thought about the text carefully and that you have learned about it.

 Language Resources
Comparison and Contrast
Ideas, events, and reasons can be compared and contrasted with the following signal words and phrases.

Compare	Contrast
similar	different from
alike	unlike
have in common	the opposite of
also	but or however
similarly	although
likewise	in contrast
	even though

Learning Targets
- Apply basic understanding of how ideas, events, or reasons are linked throughout a text using a select set of everyday connecting words or phrases to comprehending texts and writing basic texts.
- Combine clauses in a few basic ways to make connections between and join ideas (e.g., creating compound sentences using *and, but, so*).

Compare and Contrast
Part of analyzing and responding to what you read is comparing and contrasting characters, settings, and incidents in a story. In writing exposition in which you compare and contrast, you will use signal words and phrases that help the reader see what you are comparing and contrasting. Read the examples of compare and contrast signal words and phrases in the Language Resources box.

Skim through *Walk Two Moons* looking for examples of character details that you can compare and contrast. Write three examples in the chart. Then write a compound sentence that compares or contrasts the characters. Choose a word or phrase from the Language Resources list to make the comparison or contrast.

Sal's Character Details	Phoebe's Character Details	Compound Sentence
Sal is a country girl who is brave.	Phoebe is a quiet girl who thinks Sal is brave.	Sal is a country girl, but Phoebe is a quiet girl.

Quick Conversation

- Share your work with a partner. Take turns explaining your character analyses and how you compared and contrasted character details. Discuss whether your partner agrees or disagrees with your analyses. Record notes from your discussion.

> In my opinion, _____ and _____ are _____.

> Do you agree with my analysis?

> I agree with your analysis because _____.

> I disagree with your analysis because _____.

Write a Short Argument

After analyzing character details in *Walk Two Moons*, you have enough information to write a short argument. Choose one set of character details from your chart. Write a short argument in which you explain the characters are similar or different in your topic sentence, state your opinion, and give a reason why in your commentary. Before writing, read the model short argument provided. Notice what information is in each of the four sentences. Try structuring your argument in the same way.

_____

_____

_____

_____

MODEL: SHORT ARGUMENT

The narrator uses character details such as "a quiet girl who stayed mostly to herself" to describe Phoebe. Sal, the narrator, explains that she waves at Phoebe but Phoebe does not wave back, which shows that she is unlike her. These character details show the reader character traits of Phoebe and Sal. In my opinion, this character details are effective because they make the reader understand how the two characters are different.

Interacting in Meaningful Ways:
Writing an Expository Text

Language Resources

expository writing: writing that delivers information and usually includes a main idea with supporting details

technique: a method used by an author to provide readers with a deeper understanding

Learning Targets

- Express inferences and conclusions drawn based on close reading of grade-level texts and viewing of multimedia using some frequently used verbs.
- Combine clauses in a few basic ways to make connections between and join ideas.
- Read closely to explain the similarities and differences between characters.
- Write short literary and informational texts collaboratively and independently.

Review your annotations and notes on *Walk Two Moons* and use them to complete the graphic organizer.

Character's Appearance	Character's Actions	What the Character Says	What Others Say About the Character
Sal:			
Phoebe:			

Quick Conversation

Share your work with your partner. Compare the character details that you wrote about Sal and Phoebe.

Next, read aloud this dialogue from the story:

> Then one day at lunch, she slid into the seat next to me and said, "Sal, you're so courageous. You're ever so brave."

Discuss the sentences. What do they tell you about Sal and Phoebe? Record notes from your discussion.

I think Sal and Phoebe _____.

I agree/disagree because _____.

Based on _____, I think _____.

Will you please explain that?

Planning an Expository Paragraph

Use the graphic organizer to plan your own expository paragraph, comparing and contrasting Sal and Phoebe. Make notes in the Venn diagram below.

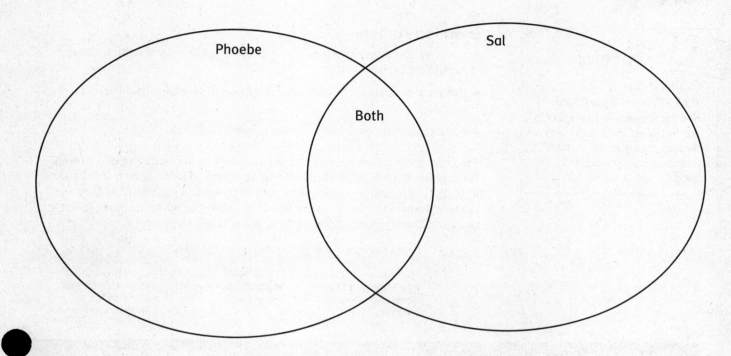

Expository Writing Prompt

Write a draft of your expository paragraph. Be sure to

- Develop a topic sentence which clearly states the main idea.
- Use adjectives and adjectival phrases to describe the traits of Sal and Phoebe.
- In your commentary, make inferences about the characters.
- Use transitional words and phrases to compare and contrast the characters of Sal and Phoebe.
- Combine clauses to create compound sentences and connect ideas.
- End with a restatement of your main idea.

_____

_____

_____

_____

_____

_____

Selecting Language Resources

WORD CONNECTIONS

Cognates

The English word *nonfiction* and the Spanish word *no ficción* are cognates. They both mean "writing that is based on facts" and come from the Latin word *fictiō*.

Learning Targets

- Develop language resources to use in one's speaking and writing about expository texts.

- Use an expanded set of words to create precision while speaking and writing.

- Adjust language choices to suit the academic setting.

The chart presents words and phrases you will use in discussion and writing. Think about each word or phrase. Circle Q, H, or T to indicate how well you know it. Work with a partner, asking your partner to explain each word or phrase. Listen closely to the explanation, and then write your partner's name in the In Our Own Words column along with his or her condensed idea.

Rating	Q	H	T
	I have seen this word or phrase, but I have **questions** about its meaning.	I have **heard** this word or phrase, but do not know it well.	I know this word or phrase so well that I could **teach** it to someone else.

Word or Phrase	Definition	In Our Own Words
nonfiction Rating Q H T	a story or writing that is based on facts or something that really happened	
author's purpose Rating Q H T	the reason that the author is writing a work: to inform, to entertain, or to persuade	
point of view Rating Q H T	the perspective from which a story is told	
supporting details Rating Q H T	facts or information that tell about a topic; they support the main idea	

Academic and Social Language Preview

Learning Target

● Develop knowledge of a growing set of academic vocabulary words to use in reading, speaking, and writing.

VOCABULARY PREVIEW

astonished: (adjective) surprised or showing wonder

astound: (verb) to cause someone to be surprised

calm: (adjective) not excited or angry

demonstrated: (verb) to prove or show something by using examples

disturb: (verb) to worry, upset, or bother someone or something

enclose: (verb) to surround or put something in or around

evidence: (noun) proof that something exists or is true

mount: (noun) a mountain or hill

opinion: (noun) someone's belief or way of thinking

reluctant: (adjective) showing doubt about something or not willing to do something

unique: (adjective) special or unlike anything else

whatever: (pronoun) anything

Vocabulary Practice

Use the definitions in the Vocabulary Preview or a dictionary to support your work.

Practice 1. Circle the word or phrase whose meaning is closest to the meaning of the vocabulary word.

Vocabulary Word	Words or Phrases to Choose From
calm	loud peaceful different
disturb	bother worry doubtful
enclose	put inside close down pull off
mount	get down get up on get ready
unique	normal hidden special
whatever	something anything nothing

Practice 2. Circle the word that best completes the sentence.

1. Her **evidence/opinion** was clear because she looked at the dress and walked away.
2. The crime scene had few clues, but there was other **evidence/opinion** to convict the thief.
3. He **demonstrated/enclosed** how to clean a bathtub with safe, natural ingredients.
4. My aunt was **reluctant/calm** to go on the trip because she would be going alone.

Practice 3. Choose the best word to complete each sentence.

1. I've never heard music like this before. It is truly _____. (astounding, unique)
2. Yesterday, I was _____ to discover that my dog had climbed a tree! (astonished, reluctant)
3. They were _____ by the loud alarm that rang in the hallway. (enclosed, astounded)
4. Please help yourself to _____ you would like to eat in our refrigerator. (whatever, opinion)

Interpret the Text Using Close Reading

Learning Target
- Express inferences and conclusions drawn based on close reading of grade-level texts and viewing of multimedia using some frequently used verbs.

Read and Annotate
Read the excerpt from *Travels with Charley* and annotate the text as you read.
- ■ Use the My Notes area to write questions or ideas you have about the story.
- ■ Underline words and phrases that help you identify the author's purpose.
- ■ Put a star next to Steinbeck's conclusion about animals.
- ■ Put an exclamation point next to details that support that conclusion.
- ■ Circle unknown words.

Memoir
from
Travels with Charley

by John Steinbeck

Chunk 1

1 I must confess to a laxness in the matter of National Parks. I haven't visited many of them. Perhaps this is because they enclose the unique, the spectacular, the astounding—the greatest waterfall, the deepest canyon, the highest cliff, the most stupendous works of man or nature. And I would rather see a good Brady photograph than Mount Rushmore. For it is my opinion that we enclose and celebrate the freaks of our nation and of our civilization. Yellowstone National Park is no more **representative** of America than is Disneyland.

2 This being my natural attitude, I don't know what made me turn sharply south and cross a state line to take a look at Yellowstone. Perhaps it was a fear of my neighbors. I could hear them say, "You mean you were that near to Yellowstone and didn't go? You must be crazy." Again it might have been the American **tendency** in travel. One goes, not so much to see but to tell afterward. Whatever my purpose in going to Yellowstone, I'm glad I went because I discovered something about Charley I might never have known.

Chunk 2

3 A pleasant-looking National Park man checked me in and then he said, "How about that dog? They aren't permitted in except on leash."

4 "Why?" I asked.

5 "Because of the bears."

6 "Sir," I said, "this is a unique dog. He does not live by tooth or fang. He respects the right of cats to be cats although he doesn't admire them. He turns his steps rather than disturb an earnest caterpillar. His greatest fear is that someone will point out a rabbit and suggest that he chase it. This is a dog of peace and tranquility. I suggest that the greatest danger to your bears will be pique at being ignored by Charley."

representative: being a typical example of a group

tendency: the fact of being likely to act in some way

prejudice: unfair treatment toward a person or group without a cause or reason

critical: likely to find fault

reform: the correction of bad conduct

My Notes

tolerance: willingness to accept others

technique: a particular method

primitive: underdeveloped

bluff: the act of deceiving or misleading

rigid: difficult or impossible to bend

encounter: meeting

7   The young man laughed. "I wasn't so much worried about the bears," he said. "But our bears have developed intolerance for dogs. One of them might demonstrate his **prejudice** with a clip on the chin, and then—no dog."

8   "I'll lock him in the back, sir. I promise you Charley will cause no ripple in the bear world, and as an old bear-looker, neither will I."

9   "I just have to warn you," he said. "I have no doubt your dog has the best of intentions. On the other hand, our bears have the worst. Don't leave food about. Not only do they steal but they are **critical** of anyone who tries to **reform** them. In a word, don't believe their sweet faces or you might get clobbered. And don't let the dog wander. Bears don't argue."

Chunk 3

10   We went on our way into the wonderland of nature gone nuts, and you will have to believe what happened. The only way I can prove it would be to get a bear.

11   Less than a mile from the entrance I saw a bear beside the road, and it ambled out as though to flag me down. Instantly a change came over Charley. He shrieked with rage. His lips flared, showing wicked teeth that have some trouble with a dog biscuit. He screeched insults at the bear, which hearing, the bear reared up and seemed to me to overtop Rocinante. Frantically I rolled the windows shut and, swinging quickly to the left, grazed the animal, then scuttled on while Charley raved and ranted beside me, describing in detail what he would do to that bear if he could get at him. I was never so astonished in my life. To the best of my knowledge Charley had never seen a bear, and in his whole history had showed great **tolerance** for every living thing. Besides all this, Charley is a coward, so deep-seated a coward that he has developed a **technique** for concealing it. And yet he showed every evidence of wanting to get out and murder a bear that outweighed him a thousand to one. I don't understand it.

Chunk 4

12   A little farther along two bears showed up, and the effect was doubled. Charley became a maniac. He leaped all over me, he cursed and growled, snarled and screamed. I didn't know he had the ability to snarl. Where did he learn it? Bears were in good supply, and the road became a nightmare. For the first time in his life Charley resisted reason, even resisted a cuff on the ear. He became a **primitive** killer lusting for the blood of his enemy, and up to this moment he had no enemies. In a bear-less stretch, I opened the cab, took Charley by the collar, and locked him in the house. But that did no good. When we passed other bears he leaped on the table and scratched at the windows trying to get out at them. I could hear canned goods crashing as he struggled in his mania. Bears simply brought out the Hyde in my Jekyll-headed dog. What could have caused it? Was it a pre-breed memory of a time when the wolf was in him? I know him well. Once in a while he tries a **bluff**, but it is a palpable lie. I swear that this was no lie. I am certain that if he were released he would have charged every bear we passed and found victory or death.

Chunk 5

13   It was too nerve-wracking, a shocking spectacle, like seeing an old, calm friend go insane. No amount of natural wonders, of **rigid** cliffs and belching waters, of smoking springs could even engage my attention while that pandemonium went on.

14   After about the fifth **encounter** I gave up, turned Rocinante about, and retraced my way. If I had stopped the night and bears gathered to my cooking, I dare not think what would have happened.

15 At the gate the park guard checked me out. "You didn't stay long. Where's the dog?"

16 "Locked up back there. And I owe you an apology. That dog has the heart and soul of a bear-killer and I didn't know it. **Heretofore** he has been a little tender-hearted toward an underdone steak."

heretofore: before now

17 "Yea!" he said. "That happens sometimes. That's why I warned you. A bear dog would know his chances, but I've seen a Pomeranian go up like a puff of smoke. You my Notes know, a well-favored bear can bat a dog like a tennis ball."

Chunk 6

18 I moved fast, back the way I had come, and I was reluctant to camp for fear there might be some unofficial non-government bears about. That night I spent in a pretty auto court near Livingston. I had my dinner in a restaurant, and when I had settled in with a drink and a comfortable chair and my bathed bare feet on the carpet with red roses, I inspected Charley. He was dazed. His eyes held a faraway look and he was totally exhausted, emotionally no doubt. Mostly he reminded me of a man coming out of a long, hard drunk—worn out, depleted, and collapsed. He couldn't eat his dinner, he refused the evening walk, and once we were in he collapsed on the floor and went to sleep. In the night I heard him whining and yapping, and when I turned on the light his feet were making running gestures and his body jerked and his eyes were wide open, but it was only a night bear. I awakened him and gave him some water. This time he went to sleep and didn't stir all night. In the morning he was still tired. I wonder why we think the thoughts and emotions of animals are simple.

My Notes

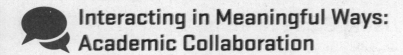

Interacting in Meaningful Ways:
Academic Collaboration

Learning Targets

- Ask and answer questions about an expository text in collaborative conversations, demonstrating active listening, and drawing upon an expanding pool of language resources for discussing literature.

- Express and support opinions in conversation.

Turn to your partner or small group to discuss each question about *Travels with Charley*. After you have discussed a question, write notes about your answer before going on to the next question.

1. What is the author's purpose in *Travels with Charley*? How do you know?

> I think the author's purpose is _____.

2. What details support the central idea in the story? Cite evidence from the story in a summary.

> The details that support the central idea are _____.

3. What words and phrases in the story help you to visualize Charley's reaction to bears?

> I think the words _____ help me to visualize it because _____.

4. How do the last three sentences of paragraph 11 contribute to the author's conclusion?

> Based on _____ I think _____.

Asking Questions

Literary nonfiction is based on facts and real events. In this memoir, Steinbeck is writing about a actual event that happened. With your partner or small group, read aloud the ending of *Travels with Charley*. Discuss what questions you have about the ending. Write one question to share with the whole class.

_____

_____

How English Works:
Verbs and Vivid Verbs

Learning Targets

- Analyze and explain in conversation and writing how vivid verbs produce effects on the reader.

- Evaluate and explain in conversation and writing how effectively the author uses vivid verbs to create imagery.

- Express and justify opinions in conversation and writing by providing text evidence and using nuanced modal expressions and phrases.

- Use a variety of verb types, tenses, and aspects appropriate for the text type and discipline on familiar topics.

Vivid Verbs

Travels with Charley is a memoir written in the first-person point of view. The narrator is the author, telling about a trip to Yellowstone National Park with his dog. The narrator uses vivid verbs to help the reader visualize their experience.

A verb is the part of speech that expresses existence, action, or occurrence. For example, They *walked* to school. Vivid verbs help to create a more precise image in the reader's mind of the action occurring. How does the action from the sentence above change your mind when you replace the verb *walked* with one of these verbs? *scrambled, skipped, marched, strode, sauntered*

⚙ Language Resources: Verbs and Vivid Verbs

Verb	Vivid Verb	Effect of Using Vivid Verb
He **moved** his body **quickly**.	He **jerked** his body.	a more precise picture of the dog moving its body in sudden sharp movements
The bear **moved quickly**.	The bear **scuttled**.	clearer to visualize the bear moving at a quick shuffling pace than just moving quickly

Skim through *Travels with Charley*, looking for sentences you like that use vivid verbs. Write three example phrases in the chart. Then write the effect of the vivid verb on your understanding and visualization.

Example Phrase with Vivid Verb	Effect
scratched at the windows trying to get out at them	I can clearly visualize Charley scratching the windows as hard as he can to attack the bears.

Create a more precise image in the sentences below by replacing the verbs with vivid verbs.

1. The dog saw a squirrel and ran after it.

2. The chef made his specialty and everyone ate happily.

 **Quick Conversation**

● Share your work with a partner. Read aloud the examples of vivid verbs that you wrote. Discuss and compare their effects on your understanding. What is the effect of using vivid verbs over verbs that are not vivid? Record notes from your discussion.

> The vivid verb _____ helps me visualize _____.

> In my opinion, the vivid verbs _____ and _____ best help me visualize the action.

> I think the vivid verb _____ is effective because _____.

Oral Presentation

Share what you learned from your discussion and the activity on the author's use of vivid verbs to help readers visualize events. Prepare a 2- or 3-minute oral presentation. Take notes on notecards to refer to during your presentation. Remember to make eye contact with your audience.

Interacting in Meaningful Ways: Analyzing Sentence Construction

Learning Target
- Engage in short written exchanges with peers and collaborate on simple written texts on familiar topics, using technology when appropriate.

Sentence Construction

John Steinbeck, the author of *Travels with Charley*, uses figurative language to create effects by engaging the reader's imagination. In this activity, you will identify, analyze, and evaluate the sentence construction in examples of figurative language.

A sentence is a word group that has both a subject and a verb that expresses a complete thought. Often an object is included. The object is a person or thing that receives the action and is often preceded by the verb. For example, John threw the ball. *Ball* is the object, *John* is the subject, and *threw* is the verb in this sentence.

Skim through *Travels with Charley* to identify sentences that use figurative language. Write four examples in the chart. Identify the subject and object in each example. Then analyze each example to understand the effect the author is trying to create.

Sentence	Subject	Object
Charley became a maniac.	Charley	maniac

Language Resources

Figurative Language: imaginative language that is not meant to be interpreted literally, but to create an effect on the reader

Subject: a person or thing that performs an action and is often followed by a verb

Object: a person or thing that receives the action and is often preceded by a verb

ACADEMIC VOCABULARY

Identify is a verb that means to recognize or find. When you read a passage, you might try to **identify** certain details or words that help you gain an understanding of what you read. For example, you might **identify** the author's purpose as to entertain readers.

Language Resources:

Sentence Construction
Sentences are usually made up of subjects, verbs, and objects. The following examples show these three different parts of the sample sentences.

Sentence
The dog likes cats. I know him well.

Subject
The dog I

Verb
likes know

Object
cats him

 **Quick Conversation**

- Share your work with a partner. Take turns sharing with your partner the sentences with subjects and objects identified. Create new sentences about Charley's reaction to the bears with your partner using proper sentence construction. Record notes from your discussion.

> I think _____.

> I heard you say _____, and I just pointed out _____.

> I agree/disagree with your sentence construction because _____.

> Will you please explain that?

Write a Short Argument

After identifying figurative language in *Travels with Charley*, you have enough information to write a short argument. Choose one sentence from your chart. Write a short argument in which you explain the meaning of it, state your opinion of how effective it is, and give a reason why. Before writing, read the model short argument provided. Notice what information is in each of the four sentences. Try structuring your argument in the same way.

_____

_____

_____

_____

MODEL: SHORT ARGUMENT

The narrator uses the sentence "Charley became a maniac" to describe how Charley changed after he saw bears. A maniac is someone who is violent or acts wildly. This is a metaphor to show the difference of Charley's behavior before and after seeing the bears. In my opinion, this metaphor is effective because it makes the reader understand exactly how seeing the bears affected Charley.

Interacting in Meaningful Ways: Writing with Purpose

Learning Target
- Write short literary and informational texts collaboratively and independently.

 Language Resources

expository writing: writing that delivers information and usually includes a main idea with supporting details
role: how the author is connected to the story
audience: who the author is writing for
format: the kind of writing the author has produced such as a story or poem
topic: the subject of what the author has written about

When identifying the author's purpose for writing a text, it is helpful to think about the role, audience, format, and topic of the text. Review your annotations and notes on *Travels with Charley* and use them to complete the RAFT graphic organizer.

ROLE	AUDIENCE
FORMAT	TOPIC

Quick Conversation

Share your work with your partner. Compare your ideas about the role, audience, format, and topic to determine the author's purpose.

Next, read aloud the last sentence of the story:

> I wonder why we think the thoughts and emotions of animals are simple.

Discuss the sentence. What does it tell you the author's conclusion is about animals? Record notes from your discussion.

I think the role was _____ because _____.

I agree/disagree with who the audience is because _____.

Based on _____, I think _____.

Will you please explain that?

Planning an Expository Paragraph

Use the RAFT graphic organizer to plan your expository paragraph.

ROLE	AUDIENCE
FORMAT	**TOPIC**

Expository Writing Prompt

Choose one of the following writing prompts:

1. Write an expository paragraph responding to Steinbeck's conclusion about animals, and evaluate his support for that conclusion.

2. Write an expository paragraph explaining your feelings about animals.

Write a draft of your expository paragraph. Be sure to

- State a strong argument.
- Include supporting details and examples.
- Use vivid verbs to help the reader visualize your points.
- Use proper sentence construction with subject and object.
- End your expository paragraph by reflecting on the author's conclusion.

_____

_____

_____

_____

_____

_____

_____

_____

_____

Selecting Language Resources

Learning Targets

- Develop language resources to use in one's speaking and writing about expository texts.

- Use an expanded set of words to create precision while speaking and writing.

- Adjust language choices to suit the academic setting.

The chart presents words and phrases you will use in discussion and writing. Think about each word or phrase. Circle Q, H, or T to indicate how well you know it. Work with a partner, asking your partner to explain each word or phrase. Listen closely to the explanation, and then write your partner's name in the In Our Own Words column along with his or her condensed idea.

WORD CONNECTIONS

Roots and Affixes

The English root word in **textual** is *text*. *Text* means "writing" or "words" as in the writing or words in a book or story. By adding the ending *–ual*, the meaning of the word changes to "relating to text."

Rating	Q	H	T
	I have seen this word or phrase, but I have **questions** about its meaning.	I have **heard** this word or phrase, but do not know it well.	I know this word or phrase so well that I could **teach** it to someone else.

Word or Phrase	Definition	In Our Own Words
introduction Rating Q H T	the opening or beginning of a story or other written work that presents the central idea or argument in a thesis statement	
hook Rating Q H T	a sentence or phrase that writers use to hook or grab the reader's attention	
thesis statement Rating Q H T	the central idea or claim being made in a written work about a topic	
textual evidence Rating Q H T	facts and details from the text that support an idea	
conclusion Rating Q H T	the ending of a story or other written work that restates the central idea or thesis statement	

Academic and Social Language Preview

Learning Target
- Develop knowledge of a growing set of academic and social vocabulary to use in reading, speaking, and writing.

VOCABULARY PREVIEW

bug: (verb) to bother

capable: (adjective) able to do something

intelligence: (noun) the ability to know, learn, or understand something, especially something difficult

monitor: (verb) to watch or check on something

offer: (verb) to give or to make something available

probably: (adverb) most likely

realize: (verb) to understand or become aware of

slightly: (adverb) a little amount

severe: (adjective) bad or serious

Vocabulary Practice
Use the definitions in the Vocabulary Preview or a dictionary to support your work.

Practice 1. Draw lines between the two academic words sharing meanings that are related.

capable   probably

slightly   intelligence

Practice 2. Complete each sentence, paying attention to the **bold** academic word.

1. She wanted to **bug** him, so she

_____

2. The teacher walked around the classroom to **monitor**

_____

3. The man's injury was so **severe** that

_____

4. I did not want to get up that morning, **probably** because

_____

5. He was **slightly** late because

_____

Practice 3. Choose the best word to complete each sentence.

1. Jamal was _____ on his way to the library when he fell off his bike.
   (slightly, probably)

2. I _____ that you are scared, but there is really nothing to be afraid of.
   (realize, offer)

3. I stood near the play area in the park, trying to _____ my brother and make sure he didn't get hurt. (bug, monitor)

Interpret the Text Using Close Reading

My Notes

Learning Target

● Express inferences and conclusions drawn based on close reading of grade-level texts and viewing of multimedia using some frequently used verbs (e.g., shows that, based on).

Read and Annotate

Read "Dogs Make Us Human" from *Animals in Translation* and annotate the text as you read.

■ Use the My Notes area to write questions or ideas you have about the story.
■ Underline words and phrases that add detail.
■ Put a star next to the authors' central idea about animals.
■ Put an exclamation mark next to details that directly support the central idea.
■ Circle unknown words.

Autobiography

"Dogs Make Us Human" from *Animals in Translation*

by Temple Grandin and Catherine Johnson

literally: actually, without exaggeration

co-evolved: evolved at the same time, having a close ecological relationship and acting as agents of natural selection for each other

1 The aborigines have a saying: "Dogs make us human." Now we know that's probably **literally** true. People wouldn't have become who we are today if we hadn't **co-evolved** with dogs.

2 I think it's also true, though in a different way, that all animals make us human. That's why I hope we will start to think more respectfully about animal intelligence and talent. That would be good for people, because there are a lot of things we can't do that animals can. We could use their help.

3 But it would be good for animals, too. Dogs first started living with people because people needed dogs and dogs needed people. Now dogs still need people, but people have forgotten how much they need dogs for anything besides love and companionship. That's probably okay for a dog who's been bred to be a companion animal, but a lot of the bigger breeds and **practically** all of the mix breeds were built for work. Having a job to do is a part of their nature; it's who they are. The sad thing is, now that hardly anyone makes his living herding sheep, most dogs are out of a job.

practically: almost, nearly

4 It doesn't have to be that way. I read a little story on the Web site for the American Veterinary Medical Association that shows the incredible things animals are capable of doing, and would do if we gave them a chance. It was about a dog named Max who had trained himself to monitor his mistress's blood sugar levels even while she was asleep. No one knows how Max was doing this, but my guess is people must smell slightly different when their blood sugar is low, and Max had figured that out. The lady who owned him was a severe diabetic, and if her blood sugar levels got low during the night Max would wake up her husband and bug him until he got up and took care of her.

5 You have to think about that story for only five seconds to realize how much dogs have to offer. Dogs and a lot of other animals.

Interact in Meaningful Ways: Academic Collaboration

Learning Targets

- Ask and answer questions about an expository text in collaborative conversations, demonstrating active listening, and drawing upon an expanding pool of language resources for discussing literature.

- Express and support opinions of an expository text in conversation.

Turn to your partner or small group to discuss each question about "Dogs Make Us Human." After you have discussed a question, write notes about your answer before going on to the next question.

1. What is the central idea in "Dogs Make Us Human"? After you have discussed it, try to summarize it in one sentence.

> I think the central idea is ____.

2. What details support the central idea? Cite textual evidence from the autobiography.

> The details that support the central idea are ____.

3. What evidence does the author use to support the central idea?

> The author uses evidence ____ to support the central idea.

4. How does the last paragraph contribute to the author's central idea about animals?

> The last paragraph contributes to the central idea by ____.

Asking Questions

Expository writing presents readers with information and explanations about a topic. Expository writing often includes a central idea and thesis statement, which is then restated at the end. With your partner or small group, read aloud the ending of "Dogs Make Us Human." Discuss what questions you have about the ending. Write one question to share with the whole class.

_____

_____

How English Works:
Dependent and Independent Clauses

Learning Targets
- Combine clauses in a few basic ways to make connections between and join ideas.
- Write short literary and informational texts (e.g., an argument for protecting the rainforests) collaboratively (e.g., with peers) and independently.

Dependent and Independent Clauses

"Dogs Make Us Human" is an autobiography written in the first-person point of view. The narrator is the author, telling about her work with animal behavior. The narrator joins dependent and independent clauses to support the central idea.

In Activity 2.13, you learned about proper sentence construction. In this activity, you will identify ways that authors combine independent clauses with dependent clauses to create complex sentences.

 Language Resources: Dependent and Independent Clauses

An independent clause can stand alone as a sentence and express a complete thought. A dependent clause does not express a complete thought and cannot stand alone as a sentence.

Dependent Clause	Independent Clause	Complex Sentence
that Aunt Kim gave us	The pear tree grows.	The pear tree that Aunt Kim gave us grows well.
When the dog was on its way home	The dog got lost on its way home.	
Because she ran	Her heart was beating fast.	

Skim through "Dogs Make Us Human" looking for sentences that combine dependent and independent clauses. Write three examples in the chart and identify the dependent and independent clause in each.

Sentence	Dependent Clause	Independent Clause
Now dogs still need people.	Now dogs still need	Now dogs still need people.

Quick Conversation

- Share your work with a partner. Read aloud the examples of dependent and independent clauses. Discuss and compare them. Explain how you could make the dependent clauses into independent clauses and how using both clauses is effective in writing. Record notes from your discussion.

> In my opinion _____.

> One difference between my idea and yours is _____.

> I think using complex sentences makes writing effective because _____.

Oral Presentation

Share what you learned from your discussion and the activity on dependent and independent clauses. Explain how it makes writing effective. Prepare a 2- or 3-minute oral presentation. Take notes on notecards to refer to during your presentation. Remember to make eye contact with your audience and speak clearly.

_____

_____

_____

_____

_____

_____

_____

_____

How English Works:
Transitions for Adding Details

Language Resources
Transition words: words that connect ideas or details

ACADEMIC VOCABULARY
Evaluate is a verb that means to judge or determine the significance, worth, or quality of something. When you read a passage you might try to evaluate certain details or words that help you gain an understanding of what you read. or example, you might evaluate whether the author effectively used transitions.

Language Resources:
Transition Words
Transition words can help you to add details to support a central idea. The following are examples of transition words and how they can be used in writing.

Compare/Add
and
also
or

Cause/Effect
so
because
therefore

Contrast
but
however
yet

Learning Target
- Combine clauses in a few basic ways to make connections between and join ideas (e.g., creating compound sentences using and, but so).

Transitions for Adding Details

The authors of "Dogs Make Us Human" use transitions, or connecting words, to add details to their writing. In this activity, you will identify, analyze, and evaluate transitions for adding details to support the central idea.

Skim through "Dogs Make Us Human" to identify sentences that use transitions to add details. Write four examples in the chart. Then analyze each example to understand the effect the authors are trying to create. Finally, think of another transition that could be used. Refer to the Language Resources list to help you.

Sentence	Analyze the Effect	Other Transition That Could Be Used
But it would be good for animals, too.	The authors want to contrast how animals needs people, too, not just that human needs animals.	however; yet

Quick Conversation

• Share your work with a partner. Take turns sharing with your partner the sentences you identified with transitions that worked well for adding details. Discuss whether your partner agrees or disagrees with the other transitions you identified that could work in the sentences. Record notes from your discussion.

> In my opinion, this transition ____.

> I agree/disagree with your choice of a transition because ____.

> Do you agree with the transition I chose? ____.

> Would you please repeat that?

Write a Short Argument

After identifying transitions in "Dogs Make Us Human," you have enough information to write a short argument. Choose one sentence from your chart. Write a short argument in which you explain the meaning of the transition and how it is used effectively to add details to support the central idea. Before writing, read the model short argument provided. Notice what information is in each of the four sentences. Try structuring your argument in the same way.

_____

_____

_____

_____

MODEL: SHORT ARGUMENT

The narrator uses the sentence "But it would be good for animals, too" to contrast the earlier detail that humans need animals. This sentence with the transition *but* adds a detail to support the central idea. In my opinion, the use of this transition to add detail is effective because it makes the reader understand that even though animals can do things that humans cannot do, animals still need humans.

Expository Essay
Informative/Explanatory Writing

Step 1: Introduction

You will be writing your own expository essay similar to others you have read in this unit such as "Dogs Make Us Human." Think about the central idea of that essay and the details that authors Temple Grandin and Catherine Johnson used to support the idea.

Expository Essay Writing Prompt:

You will write an expository essay about an important topic that you know about. Be sure to

- State a strong thesis statement with a central idea.
- Include supporting details and evidence.
- Use a variety of dependent and independent clauses.
- Use transitions to add details about the central idea.
- End your expository paragraph by restating your thesis.

Step 2: Brainstorming

Now you are ready to start thinking about what you will write about. Work in small groups or with a partner to brainstorm ideas using the graphic organizer below.

Ideas for Expository Essay	
Topic	**Central Idea/Thesis**

I think the topic I would like to write about is _____ because _____.

The aspect of the topic that is most interesting to me is _____.

A central idea I could explore is _____.

Another central idea is _____.

Expository Essay
Informative/Explanatory Writing

After your discussion, do a quickwrite paragraph of at least four to five sentences, using the following sentence frame:

The topic I want to write about is _____ . My central idea will be _____

_____

_____

_____

_____

Get together with a partner and exchange quickwrites. Read them aloud, then add more ideas to each other's quickwrites.

Discuss the ideas that you brainstormed with your partner or group. Use the sentence frames below to help you in your discussion. Remember to take turns sharing your ideas. Ask each other questions. After your discussion, draw a star next to the idea that you choose to write about.

> I think_____is a good topic because _____.

> I agree/disagree because _____.

> You can limit that topic by _____.

> You can strengthen that topic by _____.

The idea I choose to write about is _____.

Expository Essay
Informative/Explanatory Writing

My Notes

Step 3: Prewriting

Work with a partner to flesh out your ideas from your brainstorm. Talk about additional ideas you have for your expository essay. Discussing your ideas with your partner will help both of you to answer any questions that you may have.

Ask each other questions to help you gather ideas for your expository essay.

- What is the topic of the expository essay?
- What aspect of your topic will most interest readers?
- What are your strongest supporting points?
- What specific details will best support your points?
- The text evidence suggests that _____.

Record notes from your discussion. Then, based on your notes, use the graphic organizer below to begin to record your ideas.

Discussion Notes	Written by
Thesis/Central Idea: Introduction:	
Supporting Idea #1	**Possible Topic Sentence 1**
Details: Details:	
Supporting Idea #2	**Possible Topic Sentence 2**
Details: Details:	
Supporting Idea #3	**Possible Topic Sentence 3**
Details: Details:	
Conclusion:	
Restatement of Thesis:	

Expository Essay
Informative/Explanatory Writing

Step 4: Drafting

Use your completed graphic organizer and brainstorming document to help you as you begin to draft your expository essay. Remember that your draft does not have to be perfect but should include the language features that you have learned about in this unit, especially correct sentence construction, sentence variety through the use of dependent and independent clauses, transitions to add details about the central idea, and vivid verbs and adjectives.

Before you begin the draft of your expository essay, review the scoring guide with your partner so that you understand how your essay will be assessed. Ask your partner questions if you do not understand any of part of the scoring guide.

Be sure your draft has

- supporting details and evidence
- a variety of dependent and independent clauses
- transitions to connect details to the central idea
- correct sentence construction with subjects and objects
- vivid verbs and adjectives.

Step 5: Editing and Revising

Peer Editing Checklist

☐ Did the writer follow the prompt?

☐ Did the writer state a strong thesis statement with a central idea?

☐ Did the writer include supporting details and evidence?

☐ Is the writing organized in a way that makes sense?

☐ Did the writer include a variety of dependent and independent clauses?

☐ Did the writer include transitions to add details about the central idea and connect supporting paragraphs?

☐ Did the writer use correct sentence construction (subject and object)?

☐ Did the writer include vivid verbs and adjectives?

☐ Does the essay end with a restatement of the thesis?

☐ Did the writer use correct spelling and punctuation?

☐ Did the writer use correct grammar?

Look at the peer editing checklist that your partner completed and discuss it together, using these sentence frames. Takes notes on your discussion.

- I really liked _____ about the essay.
- Another thing I liked about the essay is _____.
- One part of the essay that could have been clearer is _____.
- One part of the essay that needs stronger support is _____.
- One thing I think the writer could do to improve the essay is _____.

Use your notes to help you revise your draft. Complete your revised draft on a computer, if possible. You may include graphics or photos from the Internet to include in your final draft, but make sure they are appropriate. Check your final essay against the scoring guide before you submit it to your teacher.

Language Resources
Useful Transitions in Expository Writing

Use transition words to help you to add details to support a central idea in an expository essay.

Add
and
also
or

Cause/Effect
as a result
because
so
then
therefore

Compare/Contrast
alike
but
different from
however
in contrast
likewise
on the other hand
similarly
unlike
yet

Expository Essay
Informative/Explanatory Writing

Writing Checklist

- ☐ Review the Expository Writing Rubric.
- ☐ Review the Student Expository Writing Exemplar.
- ☐ Review your draft.
- ☐ Participate in peer editing.
- ☐ Revise.
- ☐ Publish.
- ☐ Present.

Exchange drafts with your partner. Then review the scoring guide again and look at the Student Expository Text Exemplar, which you will receive from your teacher. Read each other's drafts. Use this checklist as you read your partner's draft.

Step 6: Sharing

Present your expository essay orally. You may use visual aids to make your presentation more interesting. Use the following charts to help you present and listen actively when others present their essays.

Tips for Presenting
• Practice your presentation before you give it. You can practice in front of classmates, friends, or family members.
• Speak loudly and clearly.
• Maintain eye contact with your audience.
• Listen respectfully to any questions from your audience, and respond thoughtfully to their questions.

Active Listening	
What was the presenter's purpose?	The presenter's purpose was _____.
What was the presenter's main point?	The presenter's main point was _____.
Did the presenter make eye contact?	☐ Yes ☐ No
Did the presenter use a clear, loud voice?	☐ Yes ☐ No
What is one thing you liked about the presentation?	One thing I liked about the presentation was _____.
What is a question you still have about the presentation?	A question I still have about the presentation is _____.

Step 7: Feedback

After presenting your essay orally, take the feedback you received from your classmates and make notes in the chart below. Use this feedback to plan and evaluate future presentations.

What Went Well	What Needs Improvement

Expository Essay
Informative/Explanatory Writing

SCORING GUIDE

Scoring Criteria	4	3	2	1
Ideas	The essay • responds to the prompt with a clearly focused and well sustained thesis statement • integrates relevant evidence and strong supporting details.	The essay • responds to the prompt with a focused thesis statement • integrates evidence and supporting details.	The essay • responds to the prompt with an unfocused or inconsistently sustained thesis statement • uses irrelevant or insufficient evidence and lacks supporting details.	The essay • does not respond to the prompt; response is vague or confusing • uses minimal evidence and supporting details.
Structure	The essay • introduces clearly the central idea with a strong thesis statement • uses an effective multiparagraph organizational structure • uses a variety of transitions to create coherence and integrate ideas • provides a clear restatement of the thesis in the conclusion.	The essay • introduces the central idea with a thesis statement • uses an appropriate multiparagraph organizational structure • uses transitions to create coherence • provides a restatement of the thesis statement in the conclusion.	The essay • introduces the central idea with a weak thesis • uses a flawed or inconsistent organizational structure • uses transitions ineffectively or inconsistently • provides a weak, illogical, or repetitive restatement of the thesis in the conclusion.	The essay • does not include a thesis statement in the introduction • has little or no obvious organizational structure • uses few or no transitions • lacks a conclusion.
Use of Language	The essay • uses precise and accurate diction to illustrate the topic • demonstrates command of the conventions of standard English capitalization, punctuation, spelling, grammar, and usage (including parallel structure, commas in a series, and semicolons).	The essay • uses diction that is appropriate to the topic and purpose • demonstrates adequate command of the conventions of standard English capitalization, punctuation, spelling, grammar, and usage (including parallel structure, commas in a series, and semicolons).	The essay • uses basic diction inappropriate to the topic or purpose • demonstrates partial or inconsistent command of the conventions of standard English capitalization, punctuation, spelling, grammar, and usage (including parallel structure, commas in a series, and semicolons).	The essay • uses diction that is vague or confusing • lacks command of the conventions of standard English capitalization, punctuation, spelling, grammar, and usage; frequent errors obscure meaning.

Expository Essay
Informative/Explanatory Writing

Scoring Criteria	4	3	2	1
Collaboration	Student exceeds expectations in working collaboratively with others.	Student works collaboratively with others.	Student needs development in working collaboratively with others.	Student does not work collaboratively with others.
How English Works	The essay • uses vivid verbs and adjectives consistently to help the reader visualize details.	The essay • uses vivid verbs and adjectives that help the reader visualize details.	The essay • uses weak vivid verbs and adjectives or uses them inconsistently.	The essay • lacks the use of vivid verbs and adjectives to help the reader visualize details.
Interact in Meaningful Ways	The essay • uses elaborate, accurate, and consistent sentence construction and clauses • uses strong transitions to add details that support the central idea • demonstrates command of subject-object sentence construction.	The essay • uses accurate and consistent sentence construction and clauses • uses transitions to add details that support the central idea • demonstrates understanding of subject-object sentence construction.	The essay • uses basic sentence construction and clauses • uses transitions that are ineffective in adding details that support the central idea • demonstrates partial command of subject-object sentence construction.	The essay • uses sentence construction that is inaccurate • lacks the use of transitions or clauses • lacks understanding of subject-object sentence construction.

UNIT
3

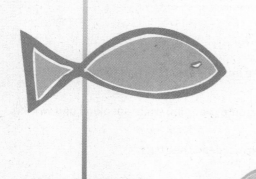

CHANGING PERSPECTIVES:
Analyzing and Creating Arguments

Visual Prompt: How do you think the perspective of the single fish is different from the perspective of the rest of the fish?

Unit Overview

To change one's perspective is to change one's viewpoint, opinion, or position about something. How many times have you tried to change someone else's mind or have others try to change your mind? In this unit, you will learn about creating an argument. Through analyzing informational and argumentative texts, you will see how others write and create argumentative texts. You will debate, and you will write your own argumentative text.

Selecting Language Resources

WORD CONNECTIONS

Suffixes

The suffix *–ment* can be added to English verbs to form nouns. The noun *argument* is formed by adding *–ment* to the verb *argue*. The nouns *judgment*, *settlement*, and *government* are formed in this way, too.

Learning Targets

- Develop language resources to use in one's speaking and writing about an argument.

- Use an expanded set of words to create precision while speaking and writing.

- Adjust language choices to suit the academic setting.

The chart presents words and phrases you will use in discussion and writing. Think about each word or phrase. Circle Q, H, or T to indicate how well you know it. Work with a partner, asking your partner to explain each word or phrase. Listen closely to the explanation, and then write your partner's name in the In Our Own Words column along with his or her condensed idea.

Rating	Q	H	T
	I have seen this literary term, but I have **questions** about its meaning.	I have **heard** this literary term but do not know it well.	I know this literary term so well that I could **teach** it to someone else.

Word or Phrase	Definition	In Our Own Words
editorial Rating Q H T	a short essay in a publication in which someone expresses an opinion on an issue	
argument Rating Q H T	a set of reasons given to persuade others that an idea or action is right or wrong	
claim Rating Q H T	a statement claiming an author's overall position on an issue	
supporting details Rating Q H T	facts and examples that develop an author's claim	
reasons Rating Q H T	the points or opinions the writer gives to show why his or her claim should be accepted	
issue Rating Q H T	an important subject or topic that people are talking about, thinking about	

Academic and Social Language Preview

Learning Target

- Develop knowledge of a growing set of academic and social vocabulary to use in reading, speaking, and writing.

VOCABULARY PREVIEW

access: (noun) the right to use or enter

awareness: (noun) knowledge; understanding

considering: (verb) thinking about

educate: (verb) teach

investigate: (verb) look into; explore

manufactured: (verb) made in a factory

pose: (verb) cause; present

proposing: (verb) suggesting

public: (adjective) having to do with the whole community

reaction: (noun) an effect or consequence

supposed: (verb) expected

trigger: (verb) cause; bring about

Vocabulary Practice

Use the definitions in the Vocabulary Preview or a dictionary to support your work.

Practice 1. Circle the word or phrase whose meaning is closest to the meaning of the vocabulary word.

Vocabulary Word	Words or Phrases to Choose From
investigate	sympathize simplify examine
supposed	purchased expected understood
educate	inform measure challenge
reaction	emotion feedback complaint
awareness	knowledge belief certainty
pose	answer cause amuse

Practice 2. Complete each sentence, paying attention to the **bold** vocabulary word.

1. To raise money, our class is **considering**

_____

2. Our principal surprised everyone by **proposing**

_____

3. To become educated, students need **access** to

_____

4. When you receive a gift, you are **supposed** to

_____

Practice 3. Choose the correct antonym to complete each sentence.

manufactured   public   trigger

1. A house is private property, while a park is _____ property.
2. Something that is made by hand is homemade. Something that is made by machines is _____ .
3. The sound of a horn will _____ the event, and the host will announce when the event is over.

Interpret the Text Using Close Reading

Learning Target
- Read closely to identify the author's claim.
- Read closely and use knowledge of word structure and context clues to determine the meaning of unknown and multiple-meaning words.

Read and Annotate

Read "Don't ban peanuts at school, but teach about the dangers" and annotate the text as you read.

■ Use the My Notes area to write questions or ideas you have about the essay.

■ Underline the supporting details.

■ Put a star next to the author's claim.

■ Circle unknown words.

Editorial

Don't ban peanuts at school, but teach about the dangers

by the Des Moines Register Editorial Board

1 Waukee school officials were considering banning peanut products for all students in kindergarten through seventh grade to try to protect children with peanut allergies. The public outcry made officials change their minds. Now the district is proposing a policy that would "strongly **discourage**" the products in schools.

2 Fine. "Strongly discouraging" may help raise awareness about the danger of nut products. Just a whiff can trigger a reaction in some people with severe allergies. Schools also can do more of what they're already doing—such as having "peanut-free" lunch tables.

3 And they can do what they do best: Educate. Schools should work with parents and students to help them learn about the life-threatening dangers nut products pose for some children.✱ Schools also should provide a list of "safe" foods to send for classroom treats.

4 Banning peanut products would be **unenforceable**.

5 Are schools going to frisk a kindergartner or search the backpack of a second grader to see if they're hiding candy with peanuts inside?

6 A student at Johnston Middle School suffered an allergic reaction to a pretzel-and-cereal trail mix from the cafeteria. It didn't even contain nuts but was exposed to peanut oils in a factory that used them in other products. Are schools supposed to investigate where prepackaged foods are manufactured and ban them if there are also nuts in the factory?

7 A ban would not ensure a child with allergies isn't exposed to harmful products. Other children will eat peanut butter for breakfast. Kids may snack on foods manufactured in a plant with peanuts.

My Notes

discourage: attempt to stop an action

unenforceable: unable to make happen

Interpret the Text Using Close Reading

8 The larger world isn't peanut free. It's important that children with peanut allergies learn to protect themselves at a young age, the same way all kids with illnesses should. Children with severe asthma may need to carry inhalers. Diabetic children need candy nearby in case their blood sugar dips too low. Children with peanut allergies should have immediate access to emergency medications to counteract an allergic reaction. School staff need to be aware of students' medical conditions and know what to do in the event of an emergency.

9 A ban would offer little beyond a false sense of security.

Interact in Meaningful Ways:
Academic Collaboration

Learning Targets

- Ask and answer questions about the author's claim in collaborative conversations, demonstrating active listening, and drawing upon an expanding pool of language resources for discussing literature.

- Express and support opinions of a topic in conversation.

- Read closely to make inferences and draw conclusions.

Turn to your partner or small group to discuss each question about "Don't ban peanuts at school, but teach about the dangers." After you have discussed a question, write notes about your answer before going on to the next question.

1. Does the title of this editorial express the author's claim? Explain why it does or doesn't.

> The title of this editorial expresses _____.

2. What details does the author use to support the claim that a peanut ban would be unenforceable?

> A peanut ban would be unenforceable because _____.

3. The author asks if schools are supposed to investigate where prepackaged foods are manufactured. How does asking this question support the claim in the editorial?

> This question is meant to show that _____.

4. Why do you think the author points out that the wider world is not peanut free?

> Pointing out that the world is not peanut free supports _____.

Asking Questions

The editorial ends with the claim that a peanut ban would give a "false sense of security." With your partner or small group, read aloud the ending in paragraph 9. Discuss what questions you have about this claim. Write one question to share with the whole class.

_____

_____

How English Works: Subject-Verb Agreement

Learning Target

● Use a variety of verb types, tenses, and aspects appropriate for the text type and discipline on familiar topics.

Subject-Verb Agreement

"Don't ban peanuts at school, but teach about the dangers" is meant to persuade readers that banning peanuts in schools is a bad idea. By using subjects that agree with the verbs in sentences, the writing is more effective and persuasive. When the subject of a sentence is singular, the writer uses the singular form of the verb. When the subject is plural, the writer uses a plural form of the verb.

⚙ Language Resources: Subject-Verb Agreement

Singular Subject	Singular Verb
The school	bans peanuts in the cafeteria.
Now the district	is proposing a new policy.
It	was exposed to peanut oil in a factory.
A parent	objected to the ban.

Plural Subject	Plural Verb
The schools	ban peanuts in the cafeteria.
Now the districts	are proposing a new policy.
They	were exposed to peanut oil in a factory.
Some parents	objected to the ban.

Underline the subject of each sentence that follows. Decide whether it is singular or plural. Then fill in the form of the verb in parentheses that agrees with the subject. Use the Language Resources: Subject-Verb Agreement chart for support.

Today the school strongly _____ peanut products in the cafeteria. (discourage)

Nut products _____ dangers for some people. (pose)

Some students _____ allergic reactions to peanuts. (suffer)

The school staff _____ to be aware of students' medical conditions. (need)

Our school _____ students about food allergies. (educate)

Schools need to _____ a list of "safe" classroom foods. (provide)

 Quick Conversation

- Share your work with a partner. Identify the subject of each sentence and whether it is singular or plural. Then discuss the verb form you used to complete the sentence. Explain why you used this form of the verb. Record notes from your discussion.

> This subject and verb do not agree because _____.

> I know the subject of this sentence is plural because _____.

> This sentence needs the singular form of the verb because _____.

Have a Short Conversation

Have a short conversation with your partner. Tell him or her about something your school does to keep students safe. On the lines write the subjects and verbs you will use. Write three singular subjects and three plural subjects. Then write the forms of the verbs that agree with the subjects.

_____

_____

_____

_____

_____

_____

_____

_____

_____

How English Works: Prepositional Phrases

Learning Targets

- Expand sentences with simple adverbials to provide details about a familiar activity or process.
- Condense ideas in simple ways or other ways of condensing to create precise and detailed sentences.

Prepositional Phrases

The author of "Don't ban peanuts at school, but teach about the dangers" uses prepositional phrases to add specific or necessary details to the sentences. Prepositional phrases function as adjectives or adverbs. They show relationships of time, location, or direction. By using prepositional phrases you can combine short choppy sentences into longer, more effective ones.

The chart that follows lists pairs of short choppy sentences. Study each pair and think of a way to combine them with a prepositional phrase. Write the new sentence in the second column.

Sentences	Combined Sentence with Prepositional Phrase
The district is proposing a new policy to discourage food products. These are foods with peanuts.	The district is proposing a new policy to discourage food products with peanuts.
The ban would not protect children. It wouldn't help students with peanut allergies.	
A student suffered an allergic reaction. It was to a pretzel-and-cereal trail mix from the cafeteria.	
It's important that allergic children learn to protect themselves. They need to learn this at a young age.	
A ban would offer little. It would offer little beyond a false sense of security.	

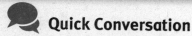

Quick Conversation

- Share your work with a partner. Take turns explaining how you combined the sentences. Point out the prepositional phrase you used in each of your sentences. Discuss whether your partner combined the sentences in the same way. Record notes from your discussion.

> In my opinion, the combined sentence is better because _____.

> I combined these sentences by_____.

> The prepositional phrase in this sentence provides details about _____.

> By combining sentences with prepositional phrases, my writing is more _____.

Write a Short Argument

Now that you've read and analyzed an editorial about banning peanuts in school cafeterias, write a short editorial/argument on some aspect of cafeteria food. In your writing, you will state your opinion and give reasons why you think it is right. Before writing, read the model short argument provided. Notice what information is in each of the four sentences. Try structuring your argument in the same way.

_____

_____

_____

_____

_____

_____

_____

_____

_____

MODEL: SHORT ARGUMENT

The school cafeteria should not have vending machines that sell soft drinks, candy, and salty snacks. Many students buy these products instead of the cafeteria lunches. Food from the vending machines—high in sugar, salt, and fats—contribute to obesity and poor health. Cafeteria lunches, by contrast, are more nutritional and healthier.

Interact in Meaningful Ways: Participating in a Debate

Learning Targets

- Negotiate with or persuade others in conversations using basic learned phrases, as well as open responses.
- Explain how well writers and speakers use language to support ideas and arguments with detailed evidence with substantial support.
- Express attitude and opinions or temper statements with some basic modal expressions (e.g., *can, has to*).

Discuss the following issue with your partner, and brainstorm pros and cons. Record them in the graphic organizer.

Should all middle school students wear uniforms?	
PRO	**CON**

After discussing the issue with your partner, pick a side and write your claim.

Sample Claim: School uniforms make students behave better.

Claim:

Rewrite your claim using modal adverbs.

High:

Low:

How do modal adverbs affect the certainty of your argument?

Planning Your Argument

Use the Graphic Organizer to plan your argument, following the claim-reason-supporting details structure of an argument.

Claim	Reasons	Supporting Details
What is my central position on this issue?	What points will persuade my readers to accept my claim?	What facts and examples support the reasons I will include?

Debating the Topic

During the debate, be sure to:

- State a clear claim.

- Support your claim with reasons and evidence; when necessary, offer new support to elaborate on a previous point.

- Maintain a formal style and appropriate tone.

- Speak clearly, slowly, and loudly enough to be heard by the audience.

- Listen to other speakers' claims, reasons, and evidence, and distinguish between claims that are supported by credible evidence and those that are not.

⚙ Language Resources: Agreeing and Disagreeing

Trying using the following types of sentence starters when you respond to the ideas of others:

Even though you just said that _____, I believe that _____.

I think that _____ is mistaken because she/he overlooks _____.

I disagree with her/his view that _____ because _____.

You make a good point about _____, and I would add that_____.

Selecting Language Resources

 WORD CONNECTIONS

Multiple Meanings

For lawyers, evidence helps prove someone is guilty or innocent. For writers, evidence helps show that a claim or argument is right.

Learning Targets

● Develop language resources to use in one's speaking and writing about news articles.

● Use an expanded set of words to create precision while speaking and writing.

● Adjust language choices to suit the academic setting.

The chart presents words and phrases you will use in discussion and writing. Think about each word or phrase. Circle Q, H, or T to indicate how well you know it. Work with a partner, asking your partner to explain each word or phrase. Listen closely to the explanation, and then write your partner's name in the In Our Own Words column along with his or her condensed idea.

Rating	Q	H	T
	I have seen this literary term, but I have **questions** about its meaning.	I have **heard** this literary term but do not know it well.	I know this literary term so well that I could **teach** it to someone else.

Word or Phrase	Definition	In Our Own Words
reasons **Rating** Q H T	the points that explain why the author is making a certain claim	
evidence **Rating** Q H T	the facts, details, and information that support the reasons for the claim	
research **Rating** Q H T	to locate reliable information from a variety of sources; the noun *research* also describes the information found from the search	
citation **Rating** Q H T	a quote of or reference to a source of evidence	

Academic and Social Language Preview

Learning Target

● Develop knowledge of a growing set of academic and social vocabulary to use in reading, speaking, and writing.

VOCABULARY PREVIEW

according: (adjective) as stated by; in agreement with

collapse: (verb) cave in

competition: (noun) a contest

competitively: (adverb) in a way that hopes to win

dangerous: (adjective) unsafe; risky

degree: (noun) level

estimate: (noun) a guess that you make based on the information you have about the size or amount of something

estimate: (verb) to make a careful guess about the size or amount of something

extremely: (adverb) very

permanent: (adjective) unending; lasting a long time

properly: (adverb) correctly; right

regulations: (noun) rules

safeguards: (noun) safety measures

whether: (conjunction) if it is true or likely that

Vocabulary Practice

Use the definitions in the Vocabulary Preview or a dictionary to support your work.

Practice 1. Circle the word or phrase whose meaning is closest to the meaning of the vocabulary word.

Vocabulary Word	Words or Phrases to Choose From
competition	a sports event a family party a school outing
dangerous	annoying risky exciting
estimate	study understand assess
permanent	difficult everlasting frequent
regulations	intentions officials guidelines
safeguards	protection guilt relaxation

Practice 2. Complete each sentence, paying attention to the **bold** vocabulary word.

1. The museum is open tonight **according** to _____

2. The house began to **collapse** when _____

3. To play a sport **competitively,** you should _____

4. At its most intense **degree,** the hurricane _____

5. I'm going to the picnic **whether** _____

Practice 3. Circle the antonym, or opposite, of each vocabulary word.
1. **extremely:**   very   slightly   usually
2. **properly:**   cleverly   interestingly   incorrectly

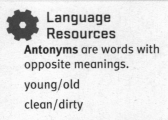

Language Resources

Antonyms are words with opposite meanings.

young/old

clean/dirty

Interpret the Text Using Close Reading

Learning Target

- Express inferences and conclusions drawn based on close reading of grade-level texts using some frequently used verbs.

Read and Annotate

Read "Most Dangerous 'Sport' of All May Be Cheerleading" by Lisa Ling and Arash Ghadishah. Annotate the text as you read.

■ Use the My Notes area to write questions or ideas you have about the story.

■ Underline words and phrases that identify the argument.

■ Put "A" next to evidence that supports one side of the argument

■ Put "B" next to evidence that supports the opposite side of the argument.

■ Circle unknown words.

News Article

Most Dangerous "Sport" of All May Be CHEERLEADING

by Lisa Ling and Arash Ghadishah

1 Two years ago, Patty Phommanyvong was a healthy 17 year old. Now she will never walk or talk again. She was injured while cheerleading—an athletic activity some say is now among the most dangerous for young girls.

2 Phommanyvong had never done any gymnastics before she started cheering. After just two months, her parents say, Patty's cheering partners were throwing her as high as 16 feet in the air.

3 Then she suffered an accident that stopped her breathing. Her parents claim that her school's **defibrillator** failed and the 45 minutes she went without oxygen left her with a brain injury that caused permanent **paralysis**. Today, Phommanyvong can only communicate by blinking.

4 One blink means yes. Twice means no. Maybe is multiple blinks.

5 Cheerleading has long been an iconic American pastime, and it is now more popular than ever. By one estimate, 3 million young people cheer, more than 400,000 at the high school level. And cheerleaders are no longer only on the sidelines—many cheer competitively.

6 The degree of difficulty of cheer stunts has exploded. So, too, has the number of accidents.

7 Cheerleading emergency room visits have increased almost sixfold over the past three decades. There were nearly 30,000 in 2008, according to the Consumer Product Safety Commission.

8 The numbers are all the more disturbing because some states don't even recognize cheerleading as a sport. That means there are no uniform safety measures and training methods.

My Notes

defibrillator: a device used to apply an electric current to the heart
paralysis: inability to move

Interpret the Text Using Close Reading

9 Kori Johnson is the cheerleading coach at Costa Mesa High School in Southern California. She says the cheerleaders have had to step up the degree of difficulty over the years.

10 "The girls, they want to be the best," said Johnson. "They want to try harder stunts. So every year when we see new stunts we try them."

Cheerleading as Competition

11 Costa Mesa High boasts a championship cheer squad.

12 Squad members say people who don't think cheerleading is a sport should just try it.

13 "They should be open minded about it," one cheerleader said. "We throw people.

14 Like our bases are lifting like people up in the air."

15 "It's like bench pressing a person," a second cheerleader said.

16 A third cheerleader said not everyone could keep up.

17 "We had the water polo boys stunt with us last year and they like, quit, after like an hour," she said. "They said it was really **intense**."

intense: extreme; having great force

'It's Scary. It's Scary.'

18 Johnson is an experienced coach with safety training and cheer certifications. She says the key to avoiding major injuries is teaching stunts step by step.

19 "I would never ask them to do a stunt that they're not capable of doing and trying," said Johnson. "So we make sure they have all the basic stunting and it's like stairs. We move up the ladder."

20 But as many parents already know, injuries are now simply a part of cheerleading.

21 "It's scary. It's scary," said Lynne Castro, the mother of a Costa Mesa cheerleader. But Castro said cheerleading was too important to her daughter to stop even after she suffered a serious injury. "You see other sports figures that have injuries and they just get on with it, you know. You fix it, you rehabilitate **properly**, and you move forward."

22 But there's no coming back from some of the injuries cheerleaders now risk. An injury is deemed catastrophic if it causes permanent spinal injury and paralysis. There were 73 of these injuries in cheerleading, including two deaths, between 1982 and 2008. In the same time period, there were only nine catastrophic injuries in gymnastics, four in basketball, and two in soccer. ...

23 In 2008, 20-year-old Lauren Chang died during a cheer competition in Massachusetts when an accidental kick to the chest caused her lungs to **collapse**.

24 "Lauren died doing what she loved, cheering and being with her friends," said Nancy Chang, her mother, soon after the accident. "We hope her death will shed light on the inherent risks of cheerleading, and we hope that additional **safeguards** are taken."

epidemic: spreading and affecting many people

25 "It's a national **epidemic**," said Kimberly Archie, who started the National Cheer Safety Foundation to campaign for more safety practices in cheerleading. "I think we should be **extremely** concerned as a nation. ... [It's] a self-regulated industry that hasn't done a good job. If I was going to give them a report card, they'd get an F in safety."

26 Cheerleading is big business. Uniform sales alone are a multimillion-dollar industry. And there are thousands of cheer events all year across the nation, with competitors from ages 3 to 23. There are cheerleading all-star teams that do not cheer for any school but compete against one another.

27 "We don't want the kids to be hurt. We want the kids to be safe," said Tammy Van Vleet, who runs the Golden State Spirit Association, which trains cheerleading coaches and runs competitions in California. "It's our priority to make sure we provide that environment. ... Since about 1999, the degree of difficulty in cheerleading has just exploded.

28 And we're seeing elite-level gymnasts on these cheerleading squads. And not just one athlete on the floor but 35 at a time, and [the] acrobatics and stunts that they are doing, you know, have not been matched."

29 That's why Van Vleet keeps two EMTs on site at major cheerleading **exhibitions**. But there are no uniform regulations that require such safety measures. ...

'What Is Safe?'

30 Jim Lord is executive director of the American Association of Cheerleading Coaches and Administrators, the largest cheerleading organization in the country. "Nightline" asked him whether cheerleading is safe.

31 "That's a great question for any sport or athletics, is, 'What is safe?'" Lord said. "There's something that says, 'Well, these are cheerleaders so they shouldn't be hurt, they shouldn't have any risks, they should be on the sidelines, and they shouldn't be doing anything'—when a lot of girls have selected this as their favorite athletic activity. And so I think there's that stigma, I think that goes along with it, for some reason."

32 Lord says that recognizing cheerleading as a sport would not increase safety and would only complicate managing an activity that is still not primarily competitive for most cheer squads.

33 "You can minimize the chance of having an injury, and what that comes down to [is] having a coach that's qualified," said Lord. "There's always going to be risk there, our job is to minimize that risk, especially from the catastrophic type of injury."

34 But Archie charges that the current system of recommended safety and training measures does not protect kids. Many cheer coaches only have to pass an open-book test to gain a safety certification.

35 Lord believes that cheerleading is not as dangerous as the injury **statistics** indicate. He says that cheerleading may look more dangerous than mainstream sports because there's no cheering season. Many cheerleaders practice all year, which means extended exposure to injury.

36 Still, critics believe that until cheerleading is recognized as a sport, safety will suffer.

37 If change is coming, it is too late for the Phommanyvongs. They are suing their daughter's school, claiming that the school did not respond properly to her injury. The school declined to comment for this story.

38 "Too far," said Patty Phommanyvong's father, Say Phommanyvong. "They went too far. They should do step by step."

39 "Maybe we can change," said her mother, Vilay. "So I don't want it to happen to another kid."

My Notes

exhibitions: public events to show something

statistic: number(s) revealing information

Interact in Meaningful Ways: Academic Collaboration

Learning Targets

- Ask and answer questions about the author's claim in collaborative conversations, demonstrating active listening, and drawing upon an expanding pool of language resources for discussing literature.

- Express and support opinions of a topic in conversation.

- Read closely to make inferences and draw conclusions.

Turn to your partner or small group to discuss each question about "Most Dangerous 'Sport' of All May Be Cheerleading." After you have discussed a question, write notes about your answer before going on to the next question.

1. How does the opening example of Patty Phommanyvong support the author's claim?

> Patty Phommanyvong proves cheerleading can be _____.

2. What evidence is offered in paragraph 7? What citation do the authors provide for this evidence?

> Paragraph 7 gives statistics about _____.

3. What evidence does Coach Lori Johnson give in paragraphs 18 and 19 to counter the authors' argument? Do you find this evidence persuasive?

> Coach Johnson claims she can avoid injuries by _____.

4. Look again at paragraphs 33–35. How do Kimberly Archie and Jim Lord use safety as a reason to support different sides of the argument about cheerleading?

> Kimberly Archie and Jim Lord disagree about _____.

Asking Questions

News articles often end by returning to an example that opened the article. With your partner or small group, read aloud the ending of the article, paragraphs 37–39. Discuss how this new information about Patty Phommanyvong supports the authors' argument. Discuss what questions you have about the ending. Write one question to share with the whole class.

_____

_____

How English Works:
Regular and Irregular Verbs

Learning Target

● Use a variety of verb types, tenses, and aspects appropriate for the text type and discipline.

Regular and Irregular Verbs

In "Most Dangerous 'Sport' of All May Be Cheerleading," the author uses strong verbs to describe what happens in cheerleading. Many verbs in English form their past and past participle forms simply by adding –d or –ed to their base form. Other verbs, called irregular verbs, change their base form in various ways to create the past and past participle.

 Language Resources: Verbs

Regular Verbs

A regular verb is one that forms its past and past participle by adding –d or –ed to its base form.

Base Form	Present Participle	Past	Past Participle
cheer	is cheering	cheered	(have) cheered
injure	is injuring	injured	have injured

Irregular Verbs

An irregular verb is one that forms its past and past participle in some way other than by adding –d or –ed to the base form.

Base Form	Present Participle	Past	Past Participle
break	is breaking	broke	(have) broken
fall	is falling	fell	have fallen
run	is running	ran	have run
throw	is throwing	threw	have thrown

Read these sentences about "Most Dangerous 'Sport' of All May Be Cheerleading." The verb in each sentence is in the present tense. Rewrite the sentence with the same verb in the past tense. Use a dictionary to check your work.

Sentences with present tense verbs	Sentences with past tense verbs
Some cheerleaders suffer accidents.	Some cheerleaders suffered accidents.
The group goes to competitions.	
The coach is giving a talk about safety.	
The cheerleaders compete with each other.	
The squad begins a new cheer.	
Many students choose cheerleading as a sport.	

Quick Conversation

- Share your work with a partner. Read aloud the original and revised sentences. Discuss how they compare. Discuss when you are most likely to use present tense verbs and when you use the past tense. Record notes from your discussion.

> The verb "go" must be irregular because _____.

> Present tense verbs tell about actions that are happening _____.

> I know "compete" is a regular verb because_____.

Give a Short Talk

Use past tense verbs to tell your partner or a small group about a problem you solved some time in the past—yesterday, last week, last year.

Next, tell about a problem that you or someone you know faces today. Use present tense verbs to explain this problem. On the writing lines, plan the verbs and sentences you will use.

_____

_____

Learning Targets

- Expand noun phrases in simple ways in order to enrich the meaning of sentences and add details about ideas, people, things, etc.

- Explain how well writers and speakers use language to support ideas and arguments with detailed evidence with substantial support.

Appositives

The authors of "Most Dangerous 'Sport' of All May Be Cheerleading" use appositives and noun phrases to add meaningful details about the people and events they describe. In this activity, you will identify, analyze, and evaluate how these phrases enrich your understanding of the article.

The chart lists four sentences from "Most Dangerous 'Sport' of All May Be Cheerleading." Underline the appositive in each sentence. Then analyze each example to understand why the appositive helps you better appreciate the information in the sentence.

 Language Resources

Appositive: a noun or pronoun placed beside another noun or pronoun to identify or explain it

Appositive phrase: an appositive and its modifiers; appositives and appositive phrases are usually set off with commas.

Noun phrase: a noun and its modifiers

Sentence with Appositive	How the Appositive Adds Meaning
She was injured while cheerleading—<u>an athletic activity some say is now among the most dangerous for young girls.</u>	explains how the authors feel about cheerleading
"It's scary," said Lynne Castro, the mother of a Costa Mesa cheerleader.	
Jim Lord is executive director of the American Association of Cheerleading Coaches and Administrators, the largest cheerleading organization in the country.	
"Lauren died doing what she loved, cheering and being with her friends," said Nancy Chang.	

Add an appositive or appositive phrase to each sentence to include more details. Use details you learned in the article.

Cheerleading today, _____, has grown rapidly.

Many cheerleaders perform stunts, _____, that are amazing.

These stunts however can lead to serious injuries, _____.

Other sports, _____, are regulated, and cheerleading should be, too.

 **Quick Conversation**

● Share your work with a partner. Take turns identifying the appositives you added and explaining why the details they add are meaningful. Discuss whether your partner agrees or disagrees with you or not. Record notes from your discussion.

> I think the appositive in this sentence is meaningful because ____.

> What details does the appositive phrase in this sentence provide?

> This appositive tells me ____.

> I think this appositive ____.

Write a Short Argument

After reading "Most Dangerous 'Sport' of All May Be Cheerleading" and evaluating its use of appositives, you have enough information to write a short argument. Write a short argument in which you explain why cheerleading should become an official sport, like football or basketball. Try to include several appositive phrases in your argument. Before writing, read the model short argument provided. Notice what information is in each of the four sentences. Try structuring your argument in the same way.

_____

_____

_____

_____

_____

_____

_____

_____

MODEL: SHORT ARGUMENT
Cheerleading, a popular school activity, should be made an official sport. Then, an official governing body, mainly experienced coaches, could set limits on unsafe cheerleading stunts. Today, these stunts, human pyramids and wild acrobatics, often cause serious or fatal injuries. Official rules, a feature of all organized sports, could ban dangerous stunts and prevent many injuries.

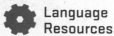

Interacting in Meaningful Ways: Writing an Argument

Learning Targets

- Write short literary and informational texts collaboratively and independently.

- Apply basic understanding of how different text types are organized to express ideas.

Reasons and Evidence

Review your annotations and notes on "Most Dangerous 'Sport' of All May Be Cheerleading." Use them to complete the graphic organizer.

> **Language Resources**
>
> **claim:** a statement claiming an author's overall position on an issue
> **reasons:** the points that explain why the author is making a certain claim
> **evidence:** the facts, details, and information that support the reasons for the claim

Side A	Side B
Claim: Cheerleading is very dangerous and needs to be regulated.	Claim: Cheerleading is not that dangerous and doesn't need to be regulated.
Reasons	Reasons
Evidence	Evidence

Quick Conversation

Share your work with your partner. Compare your reasons and evidence for each side of the argument about cheerleading. Next, read aloud these two sentences from the article.

> "[Cheerleading is] a self-regulated industry that hasn't done a good job. If I was going to give them a report card, they'd get an F in safety." —Kimberly Archie

> "You can minimize the chance of having an injury, and what that comes down to [is] having a coach that's qualified. There's always going to be risk there, ..." –Jim Lord

Discuss the sentences. What do they tell you about the two sides of the argument about cheerleading? Record notes from your discussion.

> I think the two quotes show that _____.

> I agree/disagree with _____ because _____.

> Based on _____, I think _____.

> Will you please explain that?

Planning an Argument

Use the graphic organizer to plan your own written argument, following the claim-reason-evidence text structure. Think about an issue that is important to you in your own life, and make notes about it in response to the questions that follow.

Claim	Reasons	Evidence
What is your overall position on the issue you want to argue?	What important points explain why you are making this claim?	What facts, details, and information support your reasons?

Persuasive Writing Prompt

Write a draft of your argument. Be sure to

- State your claim clearly.
- Describe at least two reasons for why you are making your claim.
- Provide evidence that supports each of your reasons.
- Use persuasive language to express your ideas.

_____

_____

_____

_____

_____

_____

_____

_____

_____

_____

Selecting Language Resources

Learning Targets

- Develop language resources to use in one's own speaking and writing about expository writing.

- Use an expanded set of words to create precision while speaking and writing.

- Adjust language choices to suit the academic setting.

The chart presents words and phrases you will use in discussion and writing. Think about each word or phrase. Circle Q, H, or T to indicate how well you know it. Work with a partner, asking your partner to explain each word or phrase. Listen closely to the explanation, and then write your partner's name in the In Our Own Words column along with his or her condensed idea.

WORD CONNECTIONS

Word Origins

The English words **pathos** and **logos** are borrowed directly from Greek. In Greek, the word *pathos* means "suffering" or "feeling," and the word *logos* means "word."

Rating	Q	H	T
	I have seen this word or phrase, but I have **questions** about its meaning.	I have **heard** this word or phrase but do not know it well.	I know this word or phrase so well that I could **teach** it to someone else.

Word or Phrase	Definition	In Our Own Words
tone Rating Q H T	the attitude that a writer or speaker displays toward his or her subject	
formal style Rating Q H T	a style of writing or speaking that is appropriate for formal communication, such as in academics or business	
rhetorical appeals Rating Q H T	persuasive strategies used in arguments to support a claim	
logos Rating Q H T	a rhetorical appeal that uses logical reasoning and evidence	
pathos Rating Q H T	a rhetorical appeal to feelings	

Academic and Social Language Preview

Learning Target
- Develop knowledge of a growing set of academic and social vocabulary to use in reading, speaking, and writing.

VOCABULARY PREVIEW

civilization: (noun) a society's stage of development

civilized: (adjective) cultured; educated

defeat: (noun) a loss in battle

duplicate: (verb) make a copy of

expression: (noun) illustration; example

generous: (adjective) substantial; large

grounds: (noun) land used for a specific purpose

lack: (noun) shortage

percent: (noun) a hundredth part of the whole

reservations: (noun) lands set aside for Native Americans

therefore: (adverb) for this or that reason

Vocabulary Practice
Use the definitions in the Vocabulary Preview or a dictionary to support your work.

Practice 1. Circle the word that is a synonym of the vocabulary word.

Vocabulary Word	Synonyms to Choose From		
civilized	wild	insincere	polite
defeat	win	tie	loss
expression	excuse	demonstration	confusion
generous	bountiful	acceptable	pleasant

Practice 2. Complete each sentence, paying attention to the **bold** vocabulary word.

1. The vacation was no fun due to a **lack** of

_____

2. I love math and science and **therefore** plan

_____

3. Our modern American **civilization** is known for

_____

4. She paid fifty **percent** of the total price, or

_____

Practice 3. Many words have multiple meanings. Circle the letter of the definition that matches the meaning of the boldfaced vocabulary word as it is used in each sentence.

1. She had won before, and she wanted to **duplicate** her success.
   a. make an exact copy of something
   b. repeat
   c. a copy made from an original

2. We were excited to make **reservations** for our vacation hotel.
   a. areas of land set aside for Native Americans
   b. doubts about doing something
   c. arrangements to have something held for you

3. Micah had no **grounds** for her argument.
   a. areas of land
   b. reasons to support a belief
   c. crushed coffee beans

My Notes

treacherous: not to be trusted

Learning Target
- Express inferences and conclusions drawn based on close reading of grade-level texts and viewing of multimedia using some frequently used verbs.

Read and Annotate
Read "The First Americans" by Scott H. Peters, Grand Council Fire American Indians. Annotate the text as you read.
- ◼ Use the My Notes area to write questions or ideas you have about the letter.
- ◼ Underline words and phrases that help you identify the author's claim.
- ◼ Put "P" next to appeals to pathos.
- ◼ Put "L" next to appeals to logos.
- ◼ Circle unknown words.

Letter

The First Americans

by Scott H. Peters, Grand Council Fire of American Indians

December 1, 1927

To the mayor of Chicago:

You tell all white men "America First." We believe in that. We are the only ones, truly, that are one hundred percent. We therefore ask you, while you are teaching schoolchildren about America First, teach them truth about the First Americans.

We do not know if school histories are pro-British, but we do know that they are unjust to the life of our people—the American Indian. They call all white victories battles and all Indian victories massacres. The battle with Custer has been taught to schoolchildren as a fearful massacre on our part. We ask that this, as well as other incidents, be told fairly. If the Custer battle was a massacre, what was Wounded Knee?

History books teach that Indians were murderers—is it murder to fight in self defense? Indians killed white men because white men took their lands, ruined their hunting grounds, burned their forests, destroyed their buffalo. White men penned our people on reservations, then took away the reservations. White men who rise to protect their property are called patriots—Indians who do the same are called murderers.

White men call Indians **treacherous**—but no mention is made of broken treaties on the part of the white man. White men say that Indians were always fighting. It was only our lack of skill in white man's warfare that led to our defeat. An Indian mother prayed that her boy be a great medicine man rather than a great warrior. It is true that we had our own small battles, but in the main we were peace loving and home loving.

White men called Indians thieves—and yet we lived in frail skin lodges and needed no locks or iron bars. White men call Indians savages. What is civilization?

Interpret the Text Using Close Reading

Its marks are a noble religion and philosophy, original arts, stirring music, rich story and legend. We had these. Then we were not savages, but a civilized race.

We made blankets that were beautiful, that the white man with all his machinery has never been able to duplicate. We made baskets that were beautiful. We wove in beads and colored quills designs that were not just decorative motifs but were the outward expression of our very thoughts. We made pottery—pottery that was useful, and beautiful as well. Why not make schoolchildren acquainted with the beautiful handicrafts in which we were skilled? Put in every school Indian blankets, baskets, pottery.

We sang songs that carried in their melodies all the sounds of nature—the running of waters, the sighing of winds, and the calls of the animals. Teach these to your children that they may come to love nature as we love it.

We had our statesmen—and their oratory[1] has never been equaled. Teach the children some of these speeches of our people, remarkable for their brilliant oratory.

We played games—games that brought good health and sound bodies. Why not put these in your schools? We told stories. Why not teach schoolchildren more of the wholesome proverbs and legends of our people? Tell them how we loved all that was beautiful. That we killed game only for food, not for fun. Indians think white men who kill for fun are murderers.

Tell your children of the friendly acts of Indians to the white people who first settled here. Tell them of our leaders and heroes and their deeds. Tell them of Indians such as Black Partridge, Shabbona, and others who many times saved the people of Chicago at great danger to themselves. Put in your history books the Indian's part in the World War. Tell how the Indian fought for a country of which he was not a citizen, for a flag to which he had no claim, and for a people that have treated him unjustly.

The Indian has long been hurt by these unfair books. We ask only that our story be told in fairness. We do not ask you to overlook what we did, but we do ask you to understand it. A true program of America First will give a generous place to the culture and history of the American Indian.

We ask this, Chief, to keep sacred the memory of our people.

My Notes

---

[1] **oratory:** Skill at public speaking

Interacting in Meaningful Ways: Academic Collaboration

Learning Targets

- Ask and answer questions about the author's claim in collaborative conversations, demonstrating active listening, and drawing upon an expanding pool of language resources for discussing literature.

- Express and support opinions of a topic in conversation.

- Read closely to make inferences and draw conclusions.

Turn to your partner or small group to discuss each question about "The First Americans." After you have discussed a question, write notes about your answer before going on to the next question.

1. What is Scott H. Peters's main claim in the letter? After discussing it, try to summarize it in one sentence.

> The author's claim in this letter is _____.

2. What examples of pathos does Scott H. Peters use to appeal to his readers' feelings? Do you think they are effective?

> The sad description of _____ appeals to my feelings.

3. What appeals to logic and reason does the letter make? What evidence does the author give to support these examples of logos?

> The author's account of _____ sounds logical because _____.

4. Evaluate the author's overall argument. Explain why you think it is or is not effective.

> Overall, the author does/does not support his claim because _____.

Asking Questions

With your partner or small group, reread the last three paragraphs of the letter. Notice that Scott H. Peters claimed history books were unfair to the first Americans. Do you think that is still true today almost 100 years after the letter was written? What questions would you ask yourself about a history textbook to find out if it was fair or not to Native Americans? Write one question to share with the whole class.

_____

_____

Interacting in Meaningful Ways: Analyzing Precise Words

Learning Objectives

- Analyze and explain in conversation and writing how precise words produce effects on the reader.

- Express and justify opinions in conversation and writing by providing text evidence and using nuanced modal expressions and phrases.

Formal Style: Precise Words

"The First Americans" is a letter written to the mayor of Chicago by an official of a Native American organization. Therefore the writer uses a formal style. **Style** is how an author uses words and phrases to form his or her ideas. A formal style tends to have precise, or exact, words.

Skim through "The First Americans," looking for sentences you like that have precise words. (Use the Precise Words chart if necessary.) Write three sentences in the chart, underlining the precise word or words in each. Then tell why you think the author used this word to make the letter to the mayor more effective. Use the Language Resources: Precise Words chart for support.

Language Resources
Precise Words

General Word	Precise Word
animals	buffalo
deals	treaties
homes	lodges
people	statesmen
property	hunting grounds
speech	oratory

Sentences with Precise Words	Why the Precise Words Are Effective
Why not teach schoolchildren more of the wholesome <u>proverbs</u> and <u>legends</u> of our people?	The precise words *proverbs* and *legends* are more precise than the words *stories* or *tales* and show the first Americans had a rich language tradition.

Quick Conversation

● Share your work with a partner. Read aloud the sentences and why you think they are effective. Discuss how they compare and which sentences you prefer. Record notes from your discussion.

> Would you agree that _____ is a precise word?

> I think the precise word _____ might be effective because _____.

> The word _____ should help readers understand the author's argument.

Have a Short Conversation

Work with a partner to create pairs of sentences that contrast general and precise nouns. One partner should say a sentence that contains one or more general nouns. For example:

The man went into the building.

The other partner then substitutes precise nouns for any general ones. For example:

The magician walked into the fun house.

Write your general and precise sentences on the lines to share with the group.

_____

_____

_____

_____

_____

_____

_____

How English Works: Passive and Active Verbs

Learning Target

- Adjust language choices according to social setting and audience.
- Use a variety of verbs types, tenses, and aspects appropriate for the text type and discipline on familiar topics.

Active and Passive Voice

The author of "The First Americans" uses mainly active voice verbs in his letter. The active voice is more direct and forceful than the passive voice. That makes it appropriate for a formal style of writing. In this activity, you will adjust and rewrite passive voice sentences to make them active.

The chart that follows lists five sentences from "The First Americans" rewritten in the passive voice. Analyze each sentence to find the subject and main verb. Then rewrite the sentence so that it is in the active voice. Check your answers in the text of the letter.

Sentence with Verb in Passive Voice	Sentence with Verb in Active Voice
The Indian has long been hurt by these unfair books.	These unfair books have long hurt the Indian.
Games were played by us—games that brought good health and sound bodies.	
Indians were called thieves by white men.	
Baskets that were beautiful were made by us.	
White men who kill for fun are thought to be murderers by Indians.	

 **Language Resources**

Active Voice Verb: a verb that expresses an action done by its subject
The first Americans told legends.
Passive Voice Verb: a verb that expresses an action done to its subject
Legends were told by the first Americans.

Language Resources

Passive Voice
The passive voice emphasizes the person or thing receiving the action rather than the one performing the action, as in the sentence, *The book was donated by a member of the community.* The passive voice is useful

when you don't know who performed an action.

when the performer is difficult to specify.

when you don't want to give away the performer's identity.

💬 Quick Conversation

- Share your work with a partner. Take turns explaining your adjustment and rewriting of the sentences. Identify the subject of each sentence, and explain why it is now performing the action in the sentence. Discuss whether your partner agrees or disagrees with your rewrites, and if necessary, check the sentence in the original letter. Record notes from your discussion.

> In this sentence the subject is _____.

> The verb _____ is in the passive voice.

> I agree/disagree with your rewrite of the sentence because _____.

> Another way to rewrite this sentence would be _____.

Write a Short Argument

In his 1927 letter, Scott H. Peters claims that school textbooks were "unjust" to the lives of Native Americans. Write a short argument in which you explain whether this claim is true or untrue today. Use details from the letter as well as what you recall from recent social studies reading. Before writing, read the model short argument provided. Notice what information is in each of the four sentences. Try structuring your argument in the same way.

_____

_____

_____

_____

_____

_____

_____

MODEL: SHORT ARGUMENT

In my opinion, modern textbooks present Native Americans fairly. My text described native cultures and their achievement, such as the irrigation systems of the Zuni people. Short excerpts from Indian statesmen, like Chief Joseph, were included in the chapter, and the book told how whites mistreated native people, such as during the Cherokees' "Trail of Tears." For these and other reasons, I think textbooks today are much fairer than in 1927.

Argumentative Letter
Argument Writing

Step 1: Introduction

In "The First Americans," Scott Peters wrote a letter to the mayor of Chicago. His letter was an argument for fairer textbooks. He tried to persuade his readers to teach schoolchildren the truth about Native Americans.

Argumentative Letter Writing Prompt:

In this lesson, you will write your own argumentative letter. Your task is to persuade your audience to accept the argument you present. To do this, your letter should:

- State clearly your claim, or overall position on an issue.

- Provide reasons for why your claim should be accepted.

- Include evidence—facts, details, and other information—that supports your reasons.

- Use a formal style and tone to present your argument.

- Include rhetorical appeals, such as logos and pathos, to make your argument more persuasive.

Step 2: Brainstorming

Work with a partner or small group of classmates to discuss possible topics for your letters. Focus on positive changes you would like to see made. You might, for example, write a letter to your school principal and argue for a change at your school. Or, perhaps your community would benefit from a certain improvement. If so, you could write to the mayor or a government official about it. As you brainstorm, try to think of issues you feel strongly about. What claim would you make for each issue? List them in the left-hand column of the chart.

Claim	Reasons	Evidence
What is your overall position on the issue?	What important points explain why you make this claim?	What facts, details, and information support your reasons?

My Notes

Argumentative Letter
Argument Writing

My Notes

Discuss the ideas that you brainstormed with your partner or group. Use the sentence frames that follow to help you in your discussion. Remember to take turns sharing your ideas and asking questions. After your discussion, draw a star next to the idea you choose to write about.

> Our school would be better if we had a ____.

> To make our community safer, I would argue for a ____.

> Who would I write to in order to change the way ____?

> I might write to persuade the president that ____.

Now try a Quickwrite on the idea you have chosen. Write an opening paragraph for your letter, and read it to a partner. Ask your partner if he or she has any ideas about how you might change the opening.

_____

_____

_____

Step 3: Prewriting

Working with a partner, share the writing ideas you have chosen. Explore your topics together, making suggestions to each other. After you decide on the claim you will make, talk about your reasons for making this claim. Also discuss what evidence you might use to support your reasons. As you talk, jot down any ideas you get for your letter.

> In my letter I plan to claim that ____.

> One reason for my claim is ____.

> What is your second reason?

> One example of evidence I could use is ____.

Argumentative Letter
Argument Writing

Based on your conversation with your partner, complete this outline for your letter. Fill in as many ideas and details as you can.

Outline of Letter of Argument

Paragraph I. Claim: _____

_____

_____

Paragraph II. First reason for claim: _____

_____

_____

   A. Evidence for first reason: _____

_____

_____

   B. Evidence for first reason: _____

_____

_____

Paragraph III. Second reason for claim: _____

_____

_____

   A. Evidence for second reason: _____

_____

_____

   B. Evidence for second reason: _____

_____

_____

Paragraph IV. Conclusion

As the outline shows, you'll need at least two reasons for making your claim. You also must give evidence to support each reason. Research is the best way to find persuasive evidence. The Internet is one place to research the supporting details you need, but be sure you use reliable websites. Books, newspapers, and magazines are good sources, too. Work with a partner to research your topics. Add any information you find to your letter outline.

Step 4: Drafting

Use your completed graphic organizer and Brainstorming document to help you as you begin to draft your argumentative letter. Remember to use the skills you practiced in Unit 3 to create precise and detailed sentences. Those skills include:

- using a variety of regular and irregular verbs.
- using modals to express opinions and meaning.

My Notes

Argumentative Letter
Argument Writing

- expanding sentences with prepositional phrases and appositives.

- using precise words.

Before you begin the first draft of your letter, work in groups to study the Scoring Guide. It shows how your letter will be scored. Discuss the points on the Scoring Guide with your classmates. As you can see, your letter should have:

- a clearly stated claim.

- strong reasons and persuasive evidence.

- a formal writing style.

- precise and detailed sentences.

- a conclusion.

Step 5: Editing and Revising

Exchange drafts with your partner. Then review the Scoring Guide again and look at the Student Argumentative Letter Text Exemplar, which you will receive from your teacher. Finally, read each other's drafts. Use this checklist as you read your partner's draft.

Peer-Editing Checklist

☐ Did the writer follow the prompt?

☐ Did the writer include a clear claim in the letter?

☐ Did the writer include reasons for the claim?

☐ Did the writer include persuasive evidence?

☐ Did the writer use a formal style of writing?

☐ Did the writer present information in a persuasive way?

☐ Did the writer use verbs that agreed with their subjects?

☐ Did the writer include precise nouns?

☐ Does the letter conclude with a restatement of the claim?

☐ Did the writer use correct spelling and punctuation?

One thing I really liked about this letter is _____.

I also thought it was effective when _____.

I thought that the claim _____.

To improve the letter, the writer could _____.

_____ would also make the letter better.

Writing Checklist
☐ Review the Student Argumentative Letter Writing Rubric.
☐ Review the Student Argumentative Letter Writing Exemplar.
☐ Review your draft.
☐ Participate in peer editing.
☐ Revise
☐ Publish
☐ Present

My Notes

Here's how the claim is worded: ____.

Where's the evidence to support this reason? ____.

The letter sounds formal except when you write ____.

One example of a precise noun is ____.

My Notes

Study the Peer-Editing checklist that your partner completed. Use it to help you revise your draft. Revise and complete your draft on a classroom computer. You may need to find more evidence from the Internet to use in your final draft. Check your final letter against the Scoring Guide before you submit it to your teacher.

Step 6: Sharing

You will now read your letter aloud. Practice your presentation at home to a family member. Keep these points in mind as you are presenting your letter:

Tips for Presenting

- Practice your presentation before you give it. You can practice in front of classmates, friends, or family members.

- Speak loudly and clearly.

- Maintain eye contact with your audience.

- Listen respectfully to any questions from your audience, and respond thoughtfully to their questions.

Argumentative Letter
Argument Writing

My Notes

Use an Active Listening chart like this to record notes for each presentation.

Active Listening	
What was the presenter's claim in the letter?	The presenter's claim was _____.
How did the presenter support the claim?	The presenter supported the claim by _____.
Did the presenter make eye contact?	☐ Yes ☐ No
Did the presenter use a clear, loud voice?	☐ Yes ☐ No
What is one thing you liked about the presentation?	One thing I liked about the presentation was ____.
What is a question you still have about the presentation?	A question I still have about the presentation is ____.

Step 7: Feedback

Keep track of the feedback—good and bad—that you get on your argumentative letter. Use a T-chart like this.

What Went Well	What Needs Improvement

Argumentative Letter
Argument Writing

SCORING GUIDE

Scoring Criteria	4	3	2	1
Ideas	The letter • supports a claim with strong reasons and persuasive evidence.	The letter • supports a claim with reasons and evidence.	The letter • has an unclear claim and lacks evidence to support its reasons.	The letter • makes no obvious claim and lacks relevant reasons and evidence.
Structure	The letter • is well-organized into paragraphs that follow smoothly and logically • includes an effective introduction and conclusion.	The letter • is organized into paragraphs. • includes an introduction and conclusion.	The letter • has a confusing or disorganized paragraph structure • lacks an introduction or a conclusion.	The letter • has little or no organization • lacks an introduction and a conclusion.
Use of Language	The letter • shows good command of a formal style • demonstrates command of the conventions of standard English capitalization, punctuation, spelling, grammar, and usage.	The letter • has a formal style • demonstrates adequate command of the conventions of standard English capitalization, punctuation, spelling, grammar, and usage.	The letter • shifts between a formal and an informal style • demonstrates partial or inconsistent command of the conventions of standard English capitalization, punctuation, spelling, grammar, and usage.	The letter • is largely informal in tone • lacks command of the conventions of standard English capitalization, punctuation, spelling, grammar, and usage; frequent errors obscure meaning.
Collaboration	Student exceeds expectations in working collaboratively with others.	Student works collaboratively with others.	Student needs development in working collaboratively with others.	Student does not work collaboratively with others.
How English Works	The letter • demonstrates full command of regular and irregular verbs, verb tense, and subject-verb agreement • makes effective use of precise words.	The letter • demonstrates good command of regular and irregular verbs, verb tense, and subject-verb agreement • makes use of precise words.	The letter • demonstrates some command of regular and irregular verbs, verb tense, and subject-verb agreement • makes little use of precise words.	The letter • demonstrates little command of regular and irregular verbs, verb tense, and subject-verb agreement • uses mainly general or vague words.

Scoring Criteria	4	3	2	1
Interact in Meaningful Ways	The letter • shows the effective use of longer sentences with clauses, prepositional phrases, and appositives • uses modals and active voice verbs to express ideas effectively.	The letter • includes longer sentences with clauses, prepositional phrases, and appositives • uses modals and active voice verbs.	The letter • includes several longer sentences • includes limited use of modals and unnecessary passive voice verbs.	The letter • includes mainly short, choppy sentences • includes frequent use of passive voice verbs.

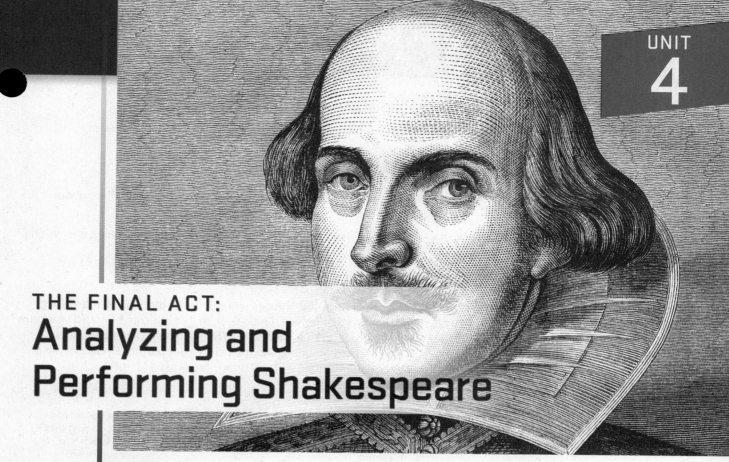

THE FINAL ACT:
Analyzing and
Performing Shakespeare

Visual Prompt: Who is this man? What clues do you see in how he is dressed? Predict how this image might relate to this last unit of study.

Unit Overview

Unit 4 introduces and gives you the opportunity to find out more about William Shakespeare, his society, and his language. The unit also extends your presentation skills and prepares you to collaborate with your classmates to perform scenes from one of Shakespeare's comedies, *The Taming of the Shrew*.

ACTIVITY 1.1

Selecting Language Resources

WORD CONNECTIONS

Cognates

The English word *explanation* and the Spanish word *explicación* are cognates. They both mean "to give reason," and come from the Latin verb *explanare*, meaning "clearly set out in words."

Learning Targets

- Develop language resources to use in one's speaking and writing about informational text.

- Use an expanded set of words to create precision while speaking and writing.

- Adjust language choices to suit the academic setting.

The chart presents words and phrases you will use in discussion and writing. Think about each word or phrase. Circle Q, H, or T to indicate how well you know it. Work with a partner, asking your partner to explain each word or phrase. Listen closely to the explanation, and then write your partner's name in the In Our Own Words column along with his or her condensed idea.

Rating	Q	H	T
	I have seen this word or phrase, but I have **questions** about its meaning.	I have **heard** this word or phrase, but I do not know it well.	I know this word or phrase so well that I could **teach** it to someone else.

Word or Phrase	Definition	In Our Own Words
research Rating Q H T	a study that is done to find out about something; the study is often done carefully, using a variety of sources	
source Rating Q H T	a person, book, periodical, or website that gives information about a topic	
summarize Rating Q H T	to tell about something in a few words or a sentence	
paraphrase Rating Q H T	to say or write something in your own words that are different from the words in a source	
synthesize Rating Q H T	to combine different things or ideas into a new idea	

Academic and Social Language Preview

Learning Target

● Develop knowledge of a growing set of academic and social vocabulary to use in reading, speaking and writing.

VOCABULARY PREVIEW

edition: (noun) a version of a book or something that is published

established: (adjective) something that has been around for a long time and has been successful

expensive: (adjective) costing a lot of money

foul: (adjective) containing marked-up corrections

foul: (adjective) having an unpleasant odor or taste

least: (noun) not less than a certain amount

public: (adjective) available to anyone

publication: (noun) something that is printed and made available for the public (people) to buy

published: (verb) a written work made available for viewing or sale

publisher: (noun) company or individual who produces books, newspapers, magazines, and other printed works

purchased: (verb) bought

reluctant: (adjective) showing doubt about doing something

role: (noun) the character that an actor or actress plays

several: (adjective) more than two but not too many

texts: (noun) pieces of writing or works with words

volume: (noun) a book or series of books

Vocabulary Practice

Use the definitions in the Vocabulary Preview or a dictionary to support your work.

Practice 1. Circle the word or phrase whose meaning is closest to the meaning of the vocabulary word.

Vocabulary Word	Words or Phrases to Choose From
expensive	cheap old costly
foul	funny smelly confused
several	little many abundant
texts	writing audio electronic
volume	closed series limited

Practice 2. Complete each sentence, paying attention to the **bold** vocabulary word.

1. He read the morning **editions** of

_____

2. The boundaries of the country were **established**, so they

_____

3. She paid the **least** amount of money to play the game and so received

_____

4. Before they left the country, they **purchased**

_____

Practice 3. Use each vocabulary word in a sentence.

1. She was _____ about going to the game because she still had to finish homework. (reluctant/established)

2. The director posted the _____ after tryouts for the play. (roles/editions)

Practice 4. The words **public, publication, published,** and **publisher** are all related words.

Choose the best word to complete each sentence below.

1. The _____ decided to offer the new author's first novel at a low introductory price.

2. Every book by that children's book author is eagerly awaited by the reading _____.

3. The popular cooking magazine is _____ once a month.

4. The most interesting new _____ is a new guide to the best science fiction movies.

Interpret the Text Using Close Reading

Learning Targets

- Express inferences and conclusions drawn based on close reading of grade-level texts and viewing of multimedia using some frequently used verbs (e.g., shows that, based on).

- Read closely and use knowledge of word structure and context clues to determine the meaning of unknown and multiple meaning words.

Read and Annotate

Read "Shakespeare's Life" from The British Library. Annotate the text as you read.

■ Use the My Notes area to write any questions or ideas you have about the text.

■ Underline words and phrases that give you information that answer these research questions: (1) Who was Shakespeare? (2) What did he accomplish? (3) When did he live? (4) Where did he live? (5) Why is he still known today?

■ Put a star next words and phrases about Shakespeare that you find interesting.

■ Put a question mark next to information that you want to research more.

■ Circle unknown words.

My Notes

Informational Text

Shakespeare's Life

from The British Library

The Key Dates

1564 Shakespeare born in Stratford-upon-Avon.

1594 Joins Lord Chamberlain's Men. *Titus Andronicus*, first quarto, published.

1599 Globe playhouse built.

1603 Death of Elizabeth I. Accession of James I.

1613 Shakespeare's writing career over.

1616 Shakespeare dies in Stratford-upon-Avon.

1623 Publication of the First Folio.

1642 Civil War closes the theatres.

1660 Theatres reopen with restoration of Charles II.

1769 Garrick's Shakespeare Jubilee in Stratford-upon-Avon.

1780 Garrick's library arrives in British Museum.

1828 George III's library arrives in British Museum.

1858 Quartos purchased from Halliwell-Phillipps.

2003 93 British Library Shakespeare quartos digitised.

2009 Digital Shakespeare quarto editions completed (107 quartos in total).

Interpret the Text Using Close Reading

My Notes

Why isn't much known about Shakespeare's life?

Who was William Shakespeare?

Shakespeare was born in Stratford-upon-Avon, Warwickshire, in 1564. Very little is known about his life, but by 1592 he was in London working as an actor and a dramatist. Between about 1590 and 1613, Shakespeare wrote at least 37 plays and collaborated on several more. Many of these plays were very successful both at court and in the public playhouses. In 1613, Shakespeare retired from the theatre and returned to Stratford-upon-Avon. He died and was buried there in 1616.

What did he write?

1 Shakespeare wrote plays and poems. His plays were comedies, histories and tragedies. His 17 comedies include _A Midsummer Night's Dream_ and _The Merry Wives of Windsor_. Among his 10 history plays are _Henry V_ and _Richard III_. The most famous among his 10 tragedies are _Hamlet, Othello_, and _King Lear_. Shakespeare's best-known poems are _The Sonnets_, first published in 1609.

What are the quartos?

Shakespeare's plays began to be printed in 1594, probably with his tragedy _Titus Andronicus_. This appeared as a small, cheap pamphlet called a quarto because of the way it was printed. Eighteen of Shakespeare's plays had appeared in quarto editions by the time of his death in 1616. Another three plays were printed in quarto before 1642. In 1623 an expensive folio volume of 36 plays by Shakespeare was printed, which included most of those printed in quarto.

Why are the quartos important?

None of Shakespeare's manuscripts survives, so the printed texts of his plays are our only source for what he originally wrote. The quarto editions are the texts closest to Shakespeare's time. Some are thought to preserve either his working drafts (his foul papers) or his fair copies. Others are thought to record versions remembered by actors who performed the plays, providing information about staging practices in Shakespeare's day.

Shakespeare in print

By the time Shakespeare began creating his plays, the London book trade was well established and growing steadily. Printing was **regulated** by the ecclesiastical authorities and the Stationers' Company, although the regulations were not always enforced. The printers, booksellers, and publishers who ran London's book trade were almost all stationers.

Printed plays formed a very small part of the book trade. Relatively few plays got into print. They did not sell in large numbers, and were not particularly profitable. The companies of players were not necessarily reluctant to have their plays printed, but the uncertainty of profits may well have deterred publishers. The dramatists themselves were unlikely to make money from the printing of their plays. There was no law of **copyright** to protect their interests. Once a manuscript play had been sold to a publisher, and he had paid for its approval and licensing for printing, he had sole rights over the work.

2 Several of Shakespeare's plays, including _Richard II_ and _Richard III_, were popular enough to be printed in several editions. From 1598, with _Love's Labour's Lost_, his name began to be added to their title-pages as a selling point. Scholars

regulated: controlled

copyright: the exclusive rights to a literary, artistic, or musical work

Interpret the Text Using Close Reading

have long held that Shakespeare had no interest in the printing of his plays, but this is now being challenged. ✗

Shakespeare's Theatre

3 Shakespeare began his career not long after the first public playhouses were established in London. His earliest plays were given at the Theatre, an open-air playhouse in Shoreditch. Many of his plays were written for the Globe, rebuilt from the timbers of the Theatre on Bankside. A number of Shakespeare's later plays were created for the very different surroundings of the indoor playhouse at Blackfriars.

Shakespeare, a player as well as a dramatist, belonged to a company of players. His company, the Lord Chamberlain's Men (from 1603 the King's Men) competed with others, notably the Admiral's Men, for audiences. Like most leading players, Shakespeare was a sharer in his company and was able to enjoy its profits. He also had to suffer its losses—for example, when the first Globe burnt down in 1613. His plays were created with his company's players in mind. Such players as the tragedian Richard Burbage and clowns like William Kemp influenced the roles within Shakespeare's plays.

4 Shakespeare's theatre came to an end in 1642. In that year, on the eve of the Civil War, all the playhouses were closed by order of Parliament. Those which were still structurally sound were either converted into **dwellings**, or demolished so that their timbers could be reused elsewhere. The players could no longer perform their plays in public.

My Notes

dwelling: a place to live

Interact in Meaningful Ways:
Academic Collaboration

Learning Targets

- Ask and answer questions about Shakespeare in collaborative conversations, demonstrating active listening, and drawing upon an expanding pool of language resources for discussing literature.

- Express and support opinions of a personal narrative in conversation.

- Read closely to make inferences and draw conclusions.

Turn to your partner or small group to discuss each question about "Shakespeare's Life." After you have discussed a question, write notes about your answer before going on to the next question.

1. What information in the text tells the reader when the Globe playhouse was built?

> The text evidence _____ indicates that _____.

2. What was important in this source's information? Write a short summary.

> I think the central idea is _____.

3. What caused Shakespeare's theatre to come to an end, according to this source?

> I think the cause was _____.

4. Cite evidence from information in the Key Dates that tells the reader about the relevance of Shakespeare's quartos.

> The text evidence _____ suggests that _____.

Asking Questions

Informational text often provides information that is well researched. With your partner or small group, read aloud one section of "Shakespeare's Life." Discuss the information that you learned from this part of the text. Write one question to pose to the whole class based on what you learned.

_____

_____

How English Works: Subordinate Conjunctions

Learning Target
- Combine clauses in a few basic ways to make connections between and join ideas (e.g., creating compound sentences using and, but so).

Subordinate Conjunctions

"Shakespeare's Life" is an informational text that tells about the life and work of Shakespeare, as well as key events during this time period. The text uses subordinate conjunctions to transition from one idea to another in the same sentence.

 ### Language Resources: Subordinating Conjunctions

although, as, as though, even though, however, just as, though, whereas, while	These subordinating conjunctions are used to acknowledge, accept, or admit something: I went for a long walk, **even though** my foot was hurting.
as, because, in order to, since, so that	These subordinating conjunctions are used to show causes: He bought her a present **because** it was her birthday.
after, as soon as, as long as, before, by the time, once, until, when, whenever, while	These subordinating conjunctions are used to show relationships of time: **Before** you leave, please wash the dishes.
even if, if, in case, provided that, unless, until	These subordinating conjunctions specify a condition: You will be late **unless** you hurry up.

Practice using subordinate conjunctions to answer the research questions about Shakespeare from Activity 3. Refer to the text in "Shakespeare's Life" to answer the questions.

Research Questions	Answer with Subordinate Conjunction
Who was Shakespeare?	Shakespeare was a playwright, **though** he was also an actor.
What did Shakespeare accomplish?	
When did Shakespeare live?	
Where did Shakespeare live?	
Why is Shakespeare still known today?	

 Language Resources

Punctuating Subordinate Clauses

Subordinate conjunctions begin subordinate, or dependent, clauses in complex sentences. There are two common patterns for writing complex sentences:

Independent Clause + Subordinate Clause:
*Shakespeare' s works are still popular **because** they present timeless characters and themes.*

Subordinate Clause + Independent Clause:
***Because** they present timeless characters and themes, Shakespeare' s works are still popular.*

Notice that when a sentence begins with a subordinate conjunction, a comma separates the subordinate clause from the independent clause.

Quick Conversation

- Share your work with a partner. Read aloud the original and revised sentences. Discuss the different subordinate conjunctions you chose to use and how they were effective in transitioning from one idea to another. Record notes from your discussion.

> In my opinion, the subordinate conjunction _____ helps to _____.

> I prefer the subordinate conjunction _____ because _____.

> I think the subordinate conjunction _____ provides an effective transition because _____.

Oral Presentation

Work with a partner to prepare a dialogue in which you share what you learned about Shakespeare from the reading selection. In your dialogue, use complex sentences with subordinate conjunctions. Start with these sentence frames and create more sentences of your own. Write your dialogue on the lines below and present your dialogue to the class.

Although we know very little about Shakespeare's life, _____ .

There are no surviving manuscripts written in Shakespeare's hand, **so**
_____ .

_____

_____

_____

_____

_____

_____

_____

_____

Interacting in Meaningful Ways:
Analyze Sentence Variety

Learning Targets

- Apply basic understanding of how ideas, events, or reasons are linked throughout a text using a select set of everyday connecting words or phrases (e.g., first/next, at the beginning) to comprehending texts and writing basic texts.

- Combine clauses in a few basic ways to make connections between and join ideas (e.g., creating compound sentences using and, but, so).

- Evaluate a writer's use of sentence variety to support their ideas.

Sentence Variety

The author of "Shakespeare's Life" uses sentence variety to keep the reader's interest and convey ideas effectively. In this activity, you will practice writing different types of sentences, as well as combine the sentences into paragraphs that connect ideas about Shakespeare's life.

Skim through "Shakespeare's Life," looking for examples of different kinds of sentences. Use the Language Resources boxes for support. Write four examples in the chart. Then identify the type of sentence each one is. Finally, analyze each example to understand the effect the author is trying to create. Use sentence variety in your analysis.

Example	Type of Sentence	Analyze Its Effect
Very little is known about his life, but by 1592 he was in London working as an actor and dramatist.	Compound sentence	It gives the reader two key facts about Shakespeare and highlights the fact that little is known about his life.

Language Resources
Dependent and Independent Clauses

Understanding the difference between dependent and independent clauses can help you construct a variety of sentences. The following are descriptions of both kinds of clauses.

Dependent Clause

A group of words that has a subject and verb but is incomplete on its own

Independent Clause

A group of words that has a subject and verb and can stand alone as a sentence

ACADEMIC VOCABULARY
Convey is a verb that means "to make known or understood." If you *convey* meaning about an idea, that means that you have made your idea known. You have communicated it.

Language Resources
Sentence Types

Simple Sentence: a sentence with one independent clause (contains a subject and verb). *I saw two cats on the porch.*

Compound Sentence: a sentence with two independent clauses joined by a semicolon or comma and a coordinating conjunction such as *and, or, but, not,* or *so. I like Indian food, but I also like Italian food.*

Complex Sentence: a sentence that combines an independent clause and a dependent clause. *After class, my friends and I played basketball.*

Compound-Complex Sentence: a sentence made from two independent clauses and one or more dependent clauses. *I like to watch movies, but I dislike my local theater, which is dirty and has uncomfortable seats.*

Quick Conversation

- Share your work with a partner. Take turns explaining the examples you found, how you determined the type of sentence each was, and your analysis of what the author was trying to convey. Discuss whether your partner agrees or disagrees with your analysis. Record notes from your discussion.

> This example is a _____ sentence because _____.

> I think _____.

> I agree/disagree with your analysis because _____.

> I think the sentence _____ is effective because _____.

Write a Short Explanatory Essay

After analyzing different types of sentences in "Shakespeare's Life," you have enough information to write a short explanatory text. Write a short explanatory essay in which you answer the research question "What did Shakespeare accomplish?" Use a variety of sentences in your response. Before writing, read the model short explanatory essay provided that responds to a different research question. Notice what information is in each of the four sentences. Try structuring your text in the same way.

_____

_____

_____

_____

MODEL: SHORT EXPLANATORY TEXT
Shakespeare was both an actor and dramatist. Though little is known about his life, his plays and poems give us some insight into the man he was, and they reveal that he was a keen observer of human nature. In many ways, his genius was to understand the human condition in all its forms. Shakespeare wrote his plays specifically for his company's players, and this shows that he was passionate about his actors and his work.

Interacting in Meaningful Ways:
Present Information Learned Through Research

Learning Targets

- Explain ideas, phenomena, processes, and text relationships (e.g., compare/contrast, cause/effect, problem/solution) based on close reading of a variety of grade-level texts and viewing of multimedia with substantial support.

- Express inferences and conclusions drawn based on close reading of grade-level texts and viewing of multimedia using some frequently used verbs (e.g., shows that, based on).

- Combine clauses in a few basic ways to make connections between and join ideas (e.g., creating compound sentences using and, but, so).

- Plan and deliver brief oral presentations on a variety of topics and content areas.

Quick Conversation

- Share your work with your partner. Compare your notes and examples from the text.

Language Resources

Copy the graphic organizer below into your notebook. Use your annotations and notes to complete it.

Who Was Shakespeare?	Notes	Examples from the Text
What did he accomplish?		
When did he live?		
Where did he live?		
Why is he still known today?		

> I think Shakespeare accomplished _____ .

> The text evidence _____ shows that _____ .

> What evidence supports your thinking?

> The text evidence indicates that _____ .

Planning a Response to Research Questions

Use the graphic organizer to plan your response to the research questions. Copy it into your notebook and then use your notes and examples from the text to help you.

	Notes	Examples from the Text
Who was Shakespeare?		
What did he accomplish?		
When did he live?		
Where did he live?		
Why is he still known today?		

Explanatory Writing Prompt

Write a response to the research questions in the form of an explanatory text. Be sure to

- Cite text evidence.
- Summarize and paraphrase the text.
- Use subordinate conjunctions to connect facts and ideas.
- Use a variety of sentences to keep your reader's interest.

_____

_____

_____

_____

_____

_____

_____

_____

_____

_____

_____

_____

_____

_____

Selecting Language Resources

Learning Targets

- Develop language resources to use in one's speaking and writing about poetry.

- Use an expanded set of words to create precision while speaking and writing.

- Adjust language choices to suit the academic setting.

The chart presents words and phrases you will use in discussion and writing. Think about each word or phrase. Circle Q, H, or T to indicate how well you know it. Work with a partner, asking your partner to explain each word or phrase. Listen closely to the explanation, and then write your partner's name in the In Our Own Words column along with his or her condensed idea.

WORD CONNECTIONS

Cognates

The English word **sensory** and the Spanish word **sensorial** are cognates. They both mean "of or relating to the senses" and come from the Latin word *sens*. The five senses are touch, smell, taste, hearing, and sight.

Rating	Q	H	T
	I have seen this word or phrase, but I have **questions** about its meaning.	I have **heard** this word or phrase, but I do not know it well.	I know this word or phrase so well that I could **teach** it to someone else.

Word or Phrase	Definition	In Our Own Words
rhythm Rating Q H T	a sound that is repeated in a pattern	
rhyme scheme Rating Q H T	a pattern of rhymes that is used in a poem	
free verse Rating Q H T	a kind of poetry that uses no rhyme	
imagery Rating Q H T	words that cause people to think of images or pictures	
sensory language Rating Q H T	words and details that are used to appeal to a reader's five senses	

Academic and Social Language Preview

Learning Target
- Develop knowledge of a growing set of academic and social vocabulary to use in reading, speaking, and writing.

VOCABULARY PREVIEW

aisle: (noun) a passage where people walk or move through

bleachers: (noun) benches that are set up like steps and are often in a stadium or gym

fingered: (verb) to feel with a finger or fingers

hissing: (verb) making a sound like a long "s"

lot: (noun) a piece of land that is used for a certain purpose like to hold cars

narrow: (adjective) long but not wide

orange: (noun) a citrus fruit

released: (verb) to stop holding or to let go of something

rouge: (noun) a red loose powder or cream that is used to give pale cheeks more color

thought: (verb) to believe something

tiered: (adjective) layered or in layers

weighted: (adjective) held down by something that is heavier

Vocabulary Practice

Use the definitions in the Vocabulary Preview or a dictionary to support your work.

Practice 1. Circle the word or phrase whose meaning is closest to the meaning of the vocabulary word.

Vocabulary Word	Words or Phrases to Choose From
fingered	felt borrowed lost
narrow	wide thin short
released	put inside pulled down set free
rouge	windmill makeup rough
tiered	layered hidden unique
weighted	understood let go held down

Practice 2. Circle the word that best completes the sentence.

1. He searched in the **aisle/bleachers** of the grocery store for his keys.

2. It was quiet outside at night except for the **rouge/hissing** of the cars on the street.

3. She parked her car in the **lot/aisle** across the street from the stadium.

4. We enjoy the fruit from the **pine/orange** tree in my grandmother's backyard.

Practice 3. Choose the best word to complete each sentence.

1. Let's go find a seat high on the _____ before the game starts. (lot/bleachers)

2. I _____ you said we could stay up late tonight to watch the show. (thought, released)

My Notes

Learning Target

- Express inferences and conclusions drawn based on close reading of grade-level texts and viewing of multimedia using some frequently used verbs (e.g., shows that, based on).

Read and Annotate

Read the poem "Oranges" by Gary Soto and annotate the text as you read.

- ■ Use the My Notes area to write questions or ideas you have about the poem.
- ■ Underline words and phrases that appeal to the senses.
- ■ Put a star next to an image that seems especially powerful to you.
- ■ Put an exclamation mark next to a figure of speech that strikes you.
- ■ Circle unknown words.

Poetry

Oranges

by Gary Soto

The first time I walked
With a girl, I was twelve,
Cold, and weighted down
With two oranges in my jacket.
5 December. Frost cracking
Beneath my steps, my breath
Before me, then gone,
As I walked toward
Her house, the one whose
10 Porch light burned yellow
Night and day, in any weather.
A dog barked at me, until
She came out pulling
At her gloves, face bright
15 With rouge. I smiled,
Touched her shoulder, and led
Her down the street, across
A used car lot and a line
Of newly planted trees,
20 Until we were breathing
Before a drugstore. We

Interpret the Text Using Close Reading

My Notes

Entered, the tiny bell
Bringing a saleslady
Down a narrow aisle of goods.
25 I turned to the candies
Tiered like bleachers,
And asked what she wanted—
Light in her eyes, a smile
Starting at the corners
30 Of her mouth. I fingered
A nickel in my pocket,
And when she lifted a chocolate
That cost a dime,
I didn't say anything.
35 I took the nickel from
My pocket, then an orange,
And set them quietly on
The counter. When I looked up,
The lady's eyes met mine,
40 And held them, knowing
Very well what it was all
About.
Outside,
A few cars hissing past,
45 Fog hanging like old
Coats between the trees.
I took my girl's hand
In mine for two blocks,
Then released it to let
50 Her unwrap the chocolate.
I peeled my orange
That was so bright against
The gray of December
That, from some distance,
55 Someone might have thought
I was making a fire in my hands.

Interacting in Meaningful Ways: Academic Collaboration

Learning Targets

- Ask and answer questions about a poem in collaborative conversations, demonstrating active listening, and drawing upon an expanding pool of language resources for discussing literature.

- Express and support opinions of a poem in conversation.

Turn to your partner or small group to discuss each question about "Oranges." After you have discussed a question, write notes about your answer before going on to the next question.

1. What imagery does the author use to describe the setting? Cite text evidence from the poem.

> The author uses _____ to describe the setting.

2. How did the author's use of sentence structure in lines 40–42 develop the plot?

> The sentence structure _____.

3. Why did the author use the phrase "I fingered a nickel in my pocket"? What effect does the use of the word *fingered* have on the meaning?

> I think the word *fingered* helps me to visualize _____.

4. How do the last six lines of the poem contribute to the plot?

> I think _____.

Asking Questions

Poems often use imagery to ignite a reader's senses and give meaning to the plot. In this poem, Soto is writing about young love. With your partner or small group, read aloud "Oranges." Discuss a question you have about an example of imagery that you found especially challenging. Write one question to share with the whole class.

_____

_____

How English Works:
Punctuation and Rhythm of the Poem

Learning Objective

● Plan and deliver a brief oral presentation on how the punctuation of a poem can create mood and dramatic effects.

Punctuation and Rhythm

In "Oranges" the narrator is the author, telling about young love from the past. The poem uses punctuation and rhythm to help the reader visualize the plot but also clues in the reader about how the lines should be read. The author uses different punctuation to create mood and dramatic effects.

⚙ Language Resources: Punctuation and Rhythm

Punctuation	Action/Effect	Example
Period [.]	Long pause/dramatic pause	I didn't say anything.
Comma [,]	Short , quick pause/fast pace of events	I fingered a nickel in my pocket, then an orange,
Em-dash [—]	Longer pause than a comma/ dramatic pause and anticipation	And asked what she wanted—

Read the poem "Oranges" aloud with the correct pauses. Use the Language Resources chart to help you. Then write three examples in the chart of lines from the poem that are short and choppy but show a change in mood. Then explain how the mood changes.

Example of Short, Choppy Sentence	Change in Mood
A dog barked at me, until She came out pulling At her gloves, face bright With rouge.	The mood changes quickly from one of loud barks to a bright, beautiful face of a young girl in love.

💬 Quick Conversation

- Share your work with a partner. Read aloud the examples of the short, choppy sentences from the poem and how the mood changed. Discuss and compare your findings and understanding. How did your reading of the lines from the poem and the punctuation affect the mood? Record notes from your discussion.

> The short, choppy sentence _____.

> In my opinion, the mood that _____ creates is _____.

> I think the mood _____ when _____.

Oral Presentation

Share what you learned from your discussion and the activity on how reading the poem's punctuation correctly helps to create or change the mood. Prepare a 2- or 3-minute oral presentation. Take notes on notecards to refer to during your presentation. Remember to make eye contact with your audience. Use the lines below to write ideas for your presentation.

_____

_____

_____

_____

_____

_____

_____

_____

Interacting in Meaningful Ways:
Analyze Sensory Language

Learning Targets
- Explain how well writers and speakers use language to support ideas and arguments with detailed evidence.
- Expand noun phrases in simple ways in order to enrich the meaning of sentences and add details about ideas, people, things, etc.

Identifying Sensory Language

Gary Soto, the author of "Oranges," uses sensory language to create mood in the poem. In this activity, you will identify phrases and sentences from the poem that use sensory language to add imagery.

Skim through "Oranges" to identify sentences that use sensory language. Write three examples in the chart. Identify the lines from the poem, as well as the sense that the language appeals to. Then use the Sensory Language Resources chart to help you revise the sentences below the chart to include sensory language.

Line with Sensory Language	Sense Used
Frost cracking beneath my steps	Touch

1. The sound from the alarm was loud. _____

2. She pulled on her warm sweater. _____

3. The dessert smelled good. _____

Language Resources

Imagery: words and phrases that create a mental image in the reader's head

Five senses: the senses—hearing, sight, taste, smell, and touch—that a person has

Language Resources

Sensory Language

Sensory language includes descriptive words that appeal to the five senses. The following are examples of sensory language.

Hearing	Sight
piercing, cracking, bubbling	glowing, faded, sparkling

Taste	Touch
juicy, spicy, sugary	fuzzy, prickly, icy

Smell
fruity, musty, sweet

💬 Quick Conversation

● Share your work with a partner. Take turns discussing with your partner the effectiveness of Soto's use of sensory language to support the theme of young love. Record notes from your discussion.

> I think the sensory word(s) ____ is/are effective because ____.

> I think the sensory language is effective because ____.

> I agree/disagree with that use of sensory language because ____.

> Would you please repeat that?

Write a Short Expository Text

After identifying effective examples of sensory language from "Oranges", you have enough information to write a short expository text. Write a short expository text in which you cite examples of sensory language from the poem that are effective in supporting the theme of young love. Before writing, read the model short expository text provided. Notice what information is in each of the four sentences. Try structuring your expository text in the same way.

_____

_____

_____

_____

_____

_____

MODEL: SHORT EXPOSITORY TEXT
Gary Soto uses sensory language in his poem "Oranges" to support the theme of young love. The line "Light in her eyes, a smile" appeals to the sense of sight. The line "I was making fire in my hands" appeals to the sense of touch. This sensory language reveals the narrator's loving feelings toward a girl.

Interacting in Meaningful Ways: Writing Poetry

Learning Target
● Write short literary and informational texts collaboratively and independently.

Review your annotations and notes on "Oranges" and use them to complete the graphic organizer.

Plot	Sensory Language/Imagery	Sentence Structure/Punctuation

Quick Conversation

Share your work with your partner. Compare your ideas about the plot, sensory language, imagery, sentence structure, and punctuation used in the poem.

Next, read aloud the last line of the poem:

> I was making a fire in my hands.

Discuss the line. How does this line use imagery, and what effect does it have? Record notes from your discussion.

> I think the imagery is _____ and it is effective because _____.

> I agree/disagree that the imagery is effective because _____.

> Based on _____, I think _____.

> Will you please explain that?

Planning a Poem

Recreate the graphic organizer below in your notebook and use it to plan your poem. Write your topic in the center space and include your ideas for the plot and the sensory language you will use in the surrounding circles.

Narrative Writing Prompt

Write a poem using sensory language and imagery. Be sure to

- Include sensory language.
- Include imagery.
- Create mood using different sentence lengths and structure.

_____

_____

_____

_____

_____

_____

_____

_____

_____

_____

Selecting Language Resources

Learning Targets
- Develop language resources to use in one's speaking and writing about drama.

- Use an expanded set of words to create precision while speaking and writing.

- Adjust language choices to suit the academic setting.

The chart presents words and phrases you will use in discussion and writing. Think about each word or phrase. Circle Q, H, or T to indicate how well you know it. Work with a partner, asking your partner to explain each word or phrase. Listen closely to the explanation, and then write your partner's name in the In Our Own Words column along with his or her condensed idea.

WORD CONNECTIONS

Roots and Affixes

The English root word in **pentameter** is *pent*. *Pent* means "five." In iambic pentameter, there are five sets of unstressed syllables followed by stressed syllables. By adding the ending *–meter*, which means "an instrument or device that is used for measuring," the meaning of the word changes to "a line of poetry that has five feet."

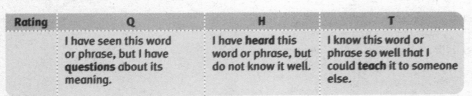

Rating	Q	H	T
	I have **seen** this word or phrase, but I have **questions** about its meaning.	I have **heard** this word or phrase, but do not know it well.	I know this word or phrase so well that I could **teach** it to someone else.

Word or Phrase	Definition	In Our Own Words
iambic pentameter Rating Q H T	a rhythm in a line of poetry that has 10 unstressed/stressed beats per line	
inflection Rating Q H T	the rise or fall of the sound of a person's voice; a change in pitch or tone	
rate Rating Q H T	the speed or pace by which something is done	
drama Rating Q H T	a play that tells a story and is performed	
oral interpretation Rating Q H T	reading aloud literature while expressing meaning of the words	

Academic and Social Language Preview

Learning Target

- Develop knowledge of a growing set of academic and social vocabulary to use in reading, speaking, and writing.

VOCABULARY PREVIEW

affable: (adjective) easy to talk to

amiss: (adverb) in the wrong way or misunderstood

burden: (noun) a heavy load or something that is very difficult to deal with

curst: (verb) past tense of *curse*; affected by something bad

enough: (adjective) what is needed

fault: (noun) weakness or defect; a flaw

rough: (adjective) difficult; not pleasant or calm

shrewd: (adjective) clever or very smart

suffice: (verb) to be enough or sufficient

thee: (pronoun) you

therefore: (adverb) because of that

thus: (adverb) because of this or like this

Vocabulary Practice

Use the definitions in the Vocabulary Preview or a dictionary to support your work.

Practice 1. Draw lines between the two vocabulary words sharing meanings that are related.

therefore   enough

suffice   thus

Practice 2. Complete each sentence, paying attention to the **bold** vocabulary word.

1. I hope that my suggestion to wear a different sweater _____ **amiss**.

2. He did not want to be a **burden** to his friends, so he

_____

3. The dog was **curst** because no matter who his owner was

_____

4. The test was **rough** because

_____

Practice 3. Choose the best word to complete each sentence.

1. Marta was _____ after the misunderstanding, and we were able to solve the problem.
   (affable, amiss)

2. His biggest _____ was that he was too trusting of others and often got his feelings hurt.
   (burden, fault)

3. I say to _____, however do you get enough sleep if you stay up all night? (thee, thus)

4. The detective was so _____ she was able to see things at the crime scene that no one else
   could. (rough, shrewd)

Interpret the Text Using Close Reading

Learning Target

- Express inferences and conclusions drawn based on close reading of a drama.

Read and Annotate

Read the excerpt from Act 1, Scene II, of *The Taming of the Shrew* by William Shakespeare. Annotate the text as you read.

- ■ Use the My Notes area to write questions or ideas you have about the drama.
- ■ Underline words and phrases that tell about the characters.
- ■ Put a star next to the plan the characters come up with.
- ■ Put exclamation marks next to figures of speech that are especially effective.
- ■ Circle unknown words.

> Drama

from THE TAMING OF THE Shrew

by William Shakespeare

Chunk 1

Act I, Scene II

Padua. Before HORTENSIO'S house
Enter PETRUCHIO *and his man* GRUMIO, *and* HORTENSIO

Hortensio: Petruchio, shall I then come roundly to thee
And wish thee to a shrewd ill-favour'd wife?
Thou'dst thank me but a little for my counsel.
And yet I'll promise thee she shall be rich,
And very rich : but thou'rt too much my friend,
And I'll not wish thee to her.

Petruchio: Signior Hortensio, 'twixt such friends as we
Few words suffice; and therefore, if thou know
One rich enough to be Petruchio's wife,
As wealth is burden of my wooing dance,
Be she as foul as was Florentius' love,
As old as Sibyl, and as curst and shrew d
As Socrates' Xanthippe or a worse,
She moves me not, or not removes, at least
Affection's edge in me, were she as rough
As are the swelling Adriatic seas.
I come to wive it wealthily in Padua;
If wealthily, then happily in Padua.

Grumio: Nay, look you, sir, he tells you flatly what his mind is. Why, give him gold enough and marry him to a puppet or an aglet-baby, or an old trot with ne'er a tooth in her head, though she have as many diseases as two and fifty horses. Why, nothing comes amiss, so money comes withal.

Hortensio: Petruchio, since we are stepp'd thus far in,
I will continue that I broach'd in jest.
I can, Petruchio, help thee to a wife
With wealth enough, and young and beauteous;
Brought up as best becomes a gentlewoman;
Her only fault, and that is faults enough,
Is that she is intolerable curst,
And shrewd and froward so beyond all measure
That, were my state far worser than it is,
I would not wed her for a mine of gold.

Chunk 2

Petruchio: Hortensio, peace. Thou know'st not gold's effect.
Tell me her father's name, and 'tis enough;
For I will board her though she chide as loud
As thunder when the clouds in autumn crack.

Hortensio: Her father is Baptista Minola,
An affable and courteous gentleman;
Her name is Katherine Minola,
Renown'd in Padua for her scolding tongue.

Petruchio: I know her father, though I know not her;
And he knew my deceased father well.
I will not sleep, Hortensio, till I see her;
And therefore let me be thus bold with you
To give you over at this first encounter—
Unless you will accompany me thither.

Grumio: [*to Hortensio*] I pray you, sir, let him go while the humour lasts. O' my word, and she knew him as well as I do, she would think scolding would do little good upon him. She may perhaps call him half a score knaves or so. Why, that's nothing; an he begin once, he'll rail in his rope-tricks. I'll tell you what, sir: an she stand him but a little, he will throw a figure in her face, and so disfigure her with it that she shall have no more eyes to see withal than a cat. You know him not, sir.

. . . Enter Gremio and Lucentio (disguised as Cambio)
Hortensio: Gremio, 'tis now no time to vent our love.
Listen to me, and if you speak me fair
I'll tell you news indifferent good for either.
[Presenting Petruchio.] Here is a gentleman whom by chance I met,

My Notes

Upon agreement from us to his liking,
Will undertake to woo curst Katherine,
Yea, and to marry her, if her dowry please.

Gremio: So said, so done, is well.
Hortensio, have you told him all her faults?

Petruchio: I know she is an irksome brawling scold.
If that be all, masters, I hear no harm.

Chunk 3

Gremio: No, sayst me so, friend? What countryman?

Petruchio: Born in Verona, old Antonio's son.
My father dead, my fortune lives for me,
And I do hope good days and long to see.

Gremio: Oh, Sir, such a life with such a wife were strange.
But if you have a stomach, to't, i' a God's name!
You shall have me assisting you in all.
But will you woo this wild-cat?

Petruchio: Will I live?

Grumio: Will he woo her? Ay, or I'll hang her.

Petruchio: Why came I hither but to that intent?
Think you a little din can daunt mine ears?
Have I not in my time heard lions roar?
Have I not heard the sea, puffed up with winds,
Rage like an angry boar chafed with sweat?
Have I not heard great ordnance in the field,
And heaven's artillery thunder in the skies?
Have I not in a pitched battle heard
Loud 'larums, neighing steeds, and trumpets' clang?
And do you tell me of a woman's tongue,
That gives not half so great a blow to hear
As will a chestnut in a farmer's fire?
Tush! tush! fear boys with bugs.

Grumio: For he fears none.

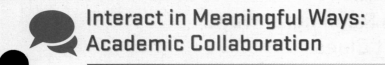

Interact in Meaningful Ways: Academic Collaboration

Learning Targets

- Ask and answer questions about a drama in collaborative conversations, demonstrating active listening, and drawing upon an expanding pool of language resources for discussing literature.

- Express and support opinions of a drama in conversation.

Turn to your partner or small group to discuss each question about *The Taming of the Shrew*. After you have discussed a question, write notes about your answer before going on to the next question.

1. What did it mean when Petruchio said, "As wealth is burden of my wooing dance" and "I come to wive it wealthily in Padua; If wealthily, then happily in Padua"?

> I think the meaning is ____.

2. What can you infer about Petruchio from these lines: "Hortensio, peace. Thou know'st not gold's effect. Tell me her father's name, and 'tis enough"?

> Based on ____, I can infer that ____.

3. Why does Shakespeare use the words "he will throw a figure in her face"? What does that phrase mean?

> Shakespeare uses the words ____ to ____.

4. Why does Hortensio call Katherine "the shrew"? What is a shrew? What context clues help you know the meaning of the word?

> I agree that it means "an unpleasant old woman," but ____.

Asking Questions

Dramas present readers with the opportunity for oral interpretation. With your partner or small group, read aloud Chunk 3 of Act 1, Scene II, from *The Taming of the Shrew*. Remember to use expression when you read as you interpret the words and their meaning. Discuss what questions you have about the end of the scene. Write one question to share with the whole class.

_____

_____

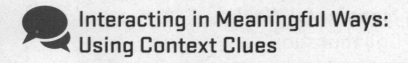

Interacting in Meaningful Ways: Using Context Clues

Learning Objective

- Use knowledge of morphology (e.g., affixes, roots, and base words), context, reference materials, and visual cues to determine the meaning of unknown and multiple-meaning words on familiar topics.

Context Clues

The Taming of the Shrew is a drama that was written by Shakespeare hundreds of years ago. It contains unfamiliar words and multiple-meaning words. To find out the meaning of these words, you can use context clues. There are different kinds of context clues to help you.

⚙ Language Resources: Context Clues

Types	Example
Comparison/Contrast	They would prefer to have the room <u>opaque</u> for the event, <u>rather than light</u>.
Details	He did not understand how to <u>assemble</u> the toy, so <u>he read the directions to find out how to put it together</u>.
Examples	She wanted to learn about <u>textiles</u> so she visited <u>a cotton company and a wool company</u>.
Multiple-Meaning Words	The <u>pitcher</u> hoped to <u>strike out the batter</u> so that there would be no more batters that inning.

Skim through *The Taming of the Shrew* looking for unfamiliar words and multiple-meaning words and their context clues. Write three examples in the chart: the sentences or phrases in which they appear, the unfamiliar word(s) or multiple-meaning word(s), and the definitions of these word(s). Underline the context clues that helped you determine the meaning of the word(s).

Sentence/Phrase	Unfamiliar Word	Definition
Were she as rough as are the swelling <u>Adriatic seas</u>	swelling	becoming large, like waves in a sea

Quick Conversation

- Share your work with a partner. Read aloud the examples of unfamiliar and multiple-meaning words and their context clues. Discuss and compare them, explaining how they helped you understand the meaning of the word. Describe the types of context clues you used. Record notes from your discussion.

> In this sentence _____ is a multiple-meaning word that means _____.

> One difference between my idea and yours is _____.

> The context clue _____ helped me understand the meaning.

Oral Presentation

Share what you learned from your discussion and the activity on using context clues to figure out the meaning of unknown words and multiple-meaning words. Explain how they helped you find the meaning of words. Prepare a 2- or 3-minute oral presentation. Use the lines below to write down your ideas. Take notes on notecards to refer to during your presentation. Remember to make eye contact with your audience and speak clearly.

_____

_____

_____

_____

_____

_____

_____

Interacting in Meaningful Ways: Identify Roots, Prefixes, and Suffixes

Language Resources

Morphology: the study of the forms of words

ACADEMIC VOCABULARY

Determine is a verb that means to find out by getting or because of facts or information. When you read a passage, you might try to **determine** the meaning of a sentence or topic. For example, you might **determine** the meaning of a word using context clues or morphology.

Language Resources

Affixes, Base Words, and Root Words

Morphology can help you determine the meaning of unknown and multiple-meaning words. The following are examples of affixes, base words, and root words.

Word	Affix (prefix)	Base/ Root	Affix (suffix)
renewable	re-	new (base)	-able
instructor		instruct (base)	-or
reinstruct	re-	instruct (base)	
cardiology		cardio (root)	-logy

Learning Target

- Use knowledge of morphology (e.g., affixes, roots, and base words), context, reference materials, and visual cues to determine the meaning of unknown and multiple-meaning words on familiar topics.

Using Morphology

We can use morphology to help determine the meaning of unknown words in *The Taming of the Shrew*. By understanding root words, affixes (such as prefixes and suffixes), and base words, we can better understand the meaning of unknown and multiple-meaning words. In this activity, you will identify, analyze, and evaluate words using morphology.

Skim through *The Taming of the Shrew* to identify sentences or phrases with unfamiliar or multiple-meaning words that have root words, affixes, or base words. Write four examples in the chart. Then analyze each example to determine the meaning of the words. Refer to the Language Resources list to help you.

Sentence/Phrase	Unfamiliar Word/ Multiple-Meaning Word	How Morphology Can Be Used to Determine the Meaning
and so disfigure her with it that she shall have no more eyes to see withal than a cat	disfigure	*figure* is root word meaning "a shape of appearance of someone's body" and *dis-* is a prefix meaning "apart, away, or having an opposing force"; *disfigure* means "to hurt the appearance of"

Quick Conversation

- Share your work with a partner. Take turns sharing with your partner the unfamiliar or multiple-meaning words and how you used morphology to help you determine their meaning. Discuss whether your partner agrees or disagrees with you. Record notes from your discussion.

> In my opinion, this word means _____ .

> I agree/disagree with how you determined the meaning because _____ .

> Do you agree with affix/root word/base word I chose?

> Would you please repeat that?

Write a Short Narrative

After identifying unfamiliar words in *The Taming of the Shrew*, you have enough information to write a short narrative. Choose one or two words from your chart. Write a short narrative in which you use those words correctly. Consider using context clues in your writing. Before writing, read the model short narrative provided. Notice what information is in each of the four sentences. Try structuring your narrative in the same way.

_____

_____

_____

_____

> **MODEL: SHORT NARRATIVE**
> The firefighter saved the child from the burning house. The child was not hurt, but flames disfigured the firefighter's face. After having surgery, the firefighter's face healed well. No one would have ever guessed that his face had been burned in a fire.

Presenting Shakespeare
Dramatic Performance

My Notes

Step 1: Introduction

You will be performing part or all of Act I, Scene 2, from *The Taming of the Shrew* by William Shakespeare. Think about the oral interpretation and expression you used when you read the scene.

Your Assignment:

You will present a scene from Shakespeare. Be sure to

- Work collaboratively to prepare and present all or part of a scene from Shakespeare's *The Taming of the Shrew*.

- Work collaboratively to make meaning of the text.

- Look for clues in the text that show how the characters would act. Model those actions In your performance.

- Create and revise a performance plan presentation.

- Plan a clear beginning, middle, and end for your presentation.

- Review and rehearse your presentation.

- Speak clearly, loudly, and slowly, with expression.

- Convey meanings of unfamiliar words.

- Maintain eye contact.

Step 2: Brainstorming

Now you are ready to start thinking about how you will plan the presentation of the scene from *The Taming of the Shrew*. Work in small groups to go over the text carefully. Brainstorm ideas for the performance using the graphic organizer below.

Notes on Character	Character's Key Lines and How to Read Them with Expression	Ideas for Character Actions	Unfamiliar Words and What They Mean

Discuss the ideas that you brainstormed with your group. Use the sentence frames below to help you in your discussion. Remember to take turns sharing your ideas. Ask each other questions. After your discussion, draw stars next to the most important ideas that you came up with.

Presenting Shakespeare
Dramatic Performance

> I don't understand the word _____ in this line.

> I agree/disagree with how you read those lines because _____.

> I think you need to read with a different expression when you say _____ and _____.

> Will you please explain why you read the character's line that way?

Step 3: Planning

Decide how your group is going to prepare to perform the scene. Which section of the scene will you perform? Will one of you act as the director, or will you share director duties? How can you fairly divide the speaking parts so that everyone gets a chance to perform?

Work with your group to talk about ideas you have for the scene. Discussing your ideas with your group will help you to answer any questions that you may have. Record notes from your discussion.

Use the graphic organizer below to begin to record your ideas.

How to Say Certain Lines	Meaning of Lines	How to Act in Character

Step 4: Practicing

Use your completed graphic organizer and brainstorming document to help you as you begin to practice your lines. Remember that you should practice your scene multiple times, using the skills that you have learned in this unit to help you. Make annotations to your script based on the decisions that you make.

Before you begin practicing, review the scoring guide with your group so that you understand how your scene will be assessed. Ask your group members questions if you do not understand any of part of the scoring guide.

My Notes

Presenting Shakespeare
Dramatic Performance

© 2017 College Board. All rights reserved.

My Notes

Be sure to keep these points in mind as you practice:

- Speak loudly, clearly, and slowly.
- Collaborate with your group members on oral interpretation.
- Use expression to engage your audience.
- Read punctuation and pauses clearly and correctly.
- Use actions that convey your character.
- Convey the meanings of unfamiliar words.

Step 5: Evaluating

Rehearse your scene before your performance. Then review the scoring guide again. Watch another group's presentation, using the Peer Evaluation Checklist.

Peer Evaluation Checklist

☐ Did the students speak loudly, clearly, and slowly?
☐ Did the students collaborate with other group members on oral interpretation?
☐ Did the students use expression to engage the audience?
☐ Did the students read punctuation and pauses clearly and correctly?
☐ Did the students convey meaning of unfamiliar words?
☐ Were there any mispronunciations?
☐ Were there any parts of the presentation that were unclear?

Two things I really liked about the presentation are

1. _____

_____

2. _____

_____

One thing I think the students could do to improve is

_____

_____

_____

_____

_____

_____

Look at the Peer Evaluation Checklist that your partner completed. Use it to help you improve your presentation. Consider using audio or visual software or equipment to enhance and record your presentation. You might also consider using simple costumes and props.

Step 6: Presenting

Present your scene using whatever visual aids or props your group decided on. Keep these points in mind as you are presenting:

Presentation Tips
• Practice your presentation before you give it.
• Speak loudly and clearly.
• Maintain eye contact with your audience.
• Use actions as well as verbal expression to portray your character.
• Use expression to convey the meaning of words that may be unfamiliar to your audience.

Active Listening	
Did the performers appear to collaborate well with one another?	
Which choices did the performers make that seemed especially effective to you?	
Did the performers make eye contact?	☐ Yes ☐ No
Did the performers use clear, loud, expressive voices and convey their characters convincingly?	☐ Yes ☐ No
What did you like best about the performance?	What I liked best about the performance was ____.
What is a question you still have about the performance?	A question I still have about the performance is ____.

My Notes

Presenting Shakespeare
Dramatic Performance

Step 7: Feedback

Keep track of the feedback that you get on your performance. Use a T-chart like this.

What Went Well	What Needs Improvement

Presenting Shakespeare
Dramatic Performance

SCORING GUIDE

Scoring Criteria	4	3	2	1
Ideas	The performance • demonstrates a deep understanding of a scene and characters • uses a variety of physical and visual elements (facial expressions, movement, props or background sounds/ images) effectively • shows evidence of extensive planning, rehearsal, and reflection.	The performance • demonstrates an adequate understanding of a scene and characters • uses some physical and visual elements (facial expressions, movement, props or background sounds/ images) to convey meaning • shows evidence of sufficient planning, rehearsal, and reflection.	The performance • demonstrates a partial or flawed understanding of a scene and characters • uses distracting or basic physical and visual elements (facial expressions, movement, props or background sounds/ images) • shows evidence of ineffective or insufficient planning, rehearsal, and reflection.	The performance • demonstrates little or no understanding of a scene and characters • lacks physical and/ or visual elements • does not show evidence of planning, rehearsal, and reflection.
Structure	The performance • depicts a significant scene with a clear beginning, middle, and end • provides an engaging introduction and conclusion.	The performance • depicts a scene with a beginning, middle, and end • provides an introduction and conclusion.	The performance • depicts a scene with an unclear beginning, middle, and/or end • provides a weak introduction and/or conclusion.	The performance • depicts a scene that is too short • lacks an introduction and/or conclusion.
Use of Language	The performer • demonstrates effective oral interpretation skills, including eye contact, volume, rate, inflection, tone, and rhythm.	The performer • demonstrates adequate oral interpretation skills, including eye contact, volume, rate, inflection, tone, and rhythm.	The performer • demonstrates inadequate oral interpretation skills.	The performer • demonstrates or ineffective oral interpretation skills.
Collaboration	The performer • demonstrates strong evidence of collaboration.	The performer • demonstrates adequate evidence of collaboration.	The performer • demonstrates uneven or ineffective collaboration.	The performer • demonstrates a failure to collaborate.

Presenting Shakespeare
Dramatic Performance

Scoring Criteria	4	3	2	1
How English Works	The performer • uses punctuation cues (periods, commas, semicolons, dashes, exclamation points) and pauses accurately and consistently to inform vocal delivery.	The performer • uses some punctuation cues (periods, commas, semicolons, dashes, exclamation points) and pauses to inform vocal delivery.	The performer • uses punctuation cues (periods, commas, semicolons, dashes, exclamation points) and pauses unevenly or inconsistently.	The performer • does not recognize punctuation cues or pauses, or uses them incorrectly.
Interact in Meaningful Ways	The performer • consistently conveys meaning and comprehension of unfamiliar words.	The performer • consistently conveys meaning and comprehension of unfamiliar words.	The performer • is inconsistent in conveying meaning and comprehension of unfamiliar words.	The performer • does not convey meaning and comprehension of unfamiliar words.

Resources

Active Listening Feedback

Presenter's name: _____

Content

What is the presenter's purpose? _____

What is the presenter's main point? _____

Do you agree with the presenter? Why or why not? _____

_____

_____

Form

Did the presenter use a clear, loud voice? ☐ yes ☐ no

Did the presenter make eye contact? ☐ yes ☐ no

One thing I really liked about the presentation:

_____

_____

_____

One question I still have:

_____

_____

_____

Other comments or notes:

_____ DATE _____

Active Listening Notes

Title: _____

Who?

What?

Where?

When?

Why?

How?

Cause and Effect

Title: _____

| **Cause:** What happened? | → | **Effect:** An effect of this is |

| **Cause:** What happened? | → | **Effect:** An effect of this is |

| **Cause:** What happened? | → | **Effect:** An effect of this is |

| **Cause:** What happened? | → | **Effect:** An effect of this is |

Character Map

Character name: _____

What does the character look like?

How does the character act?

What do other characters say or think about the character?

Collaborative Dialogue

Title: _____

"Wh-" Prompts
Who?   What?   Where?
When?   Why?

Speaker 1

Speaker 2

Conclusion Builder

Evidence

Evidence

Evidence

Based on this evidence, I can conclude

NAME _____ DATE _____

Conflict Map

Title: _____

What is the main conflict in this story?

What causes this conflict?

How is the conflict resolved?

What are some other ways the conflict could have been resolved?

Conversation for Quickwrite

1. Turn to a partner and restate the Quickwrite in your own words.

2. Brainstorm key words to use in your Quickwrite response.

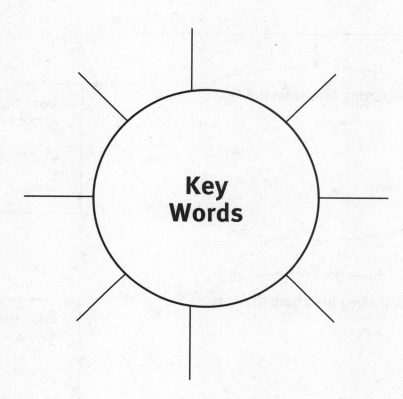

Key Words

3. Take turns explaining your Quickwrite response to your partner. Try using some of the key words.

4. On your own, write a response to the Quickwrite.

Idea and Argument Evaluator

What is the author's idea or argument?

↓

Supporting Idea from the Text

Does the author give a reason?

❑ yes

❑ no

↓

Supporting Idea from the Text

Does the author give a reason?

❑ yes

❑ no

↓

Supporting Idea from the Text

Does the author give a reason?

❑ yes

❑ no

Idea Connector

Directions: Write two simple sentences about the same topic. Next, write transition words around the Idea Connector. Then, choose an appropriate word to connect ideas in the two sentences. Write your combined sentence in the space below.

Sentence One

Sentence Two

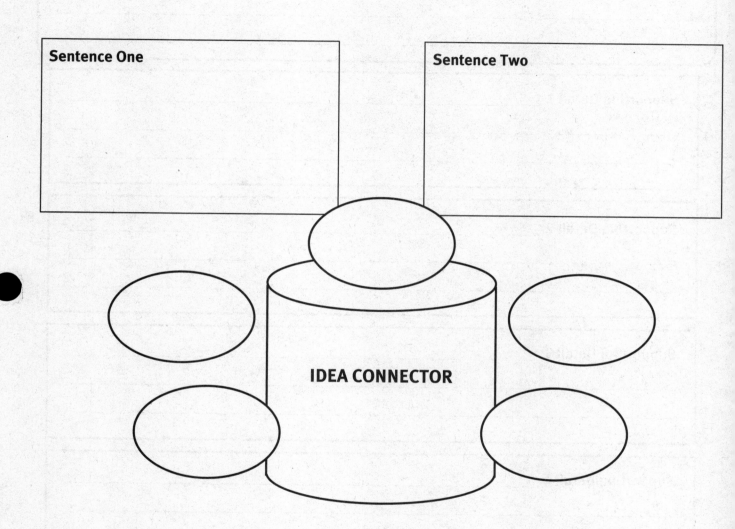

IDEA CONNECTOR

Combined Sentence

Key Idea and Details Chart

Title/Topic _____

Key Idea _____
_____
_____

Supporting Detail 1 _____
_____
_____

Supporting Detail 2 _____
_____
_____

Supporting Detail 3 _____
_____
_____

Supporting Detail 4 _____
_____
_____

Restate topic sentence. _____
_____

Concluding sentence. _____
_____
_____

Narrative Analysis and Writing

Response

Response

Incident

Reflection

Reflection

Notes for Reading Independently

Title: _____

The main characters are	The setting is	The main conflict is

The climax happens when	The conflict is resolved when

My brief summary of _____

Opinion Builder

Reason

Reason

Based on these reasons, my opinion is

Reason

Reason

Paragraph Frame for Conclusions

Conclusion Words and Phrases

shows that

based on

suggests that

leads to

indicates that

influences

The _____ (story, poem, play, passage, etc.)
shows that (helps us to conclude that) _____
_____
_____

There are several reasons why. First, _____
_____
_____
_____
_____
_____

A second reason is _____
_____
_____
_____
_____
_____

Finally, _____
_____
_____
_____
_____

In conclusion, _____
_____
_____
_____
_____

Paragraph Frame for Sequencing

Sequence Words and Phrases

at the beginning

in the first place

as a result

later

eventually

in the end

lastly

In the _____ (story, poem, play, passage, etc.)

there are three important _____

(events, steps, directions, etc.)

First, _____

_____

_____

_____

_____

Second, _____

_____

_____

_____

_____

Third, _____

_____

_____

_____

_____

Finally, _____

_____

_____

_____

_____

Paraphrasing Map

What does _____ say?	How can I say it in my own words?	What questions or response do I have?

Peer Editing

Writer's name: _____

Did the writer answer the prompt? ☐ yes ☐ no

Did the writer provide evidence to support his or her reasons? ☐ yes ☐ no

Is the writing organized in a way that makes sense? ☐ yes ☐ no

Did the writer vary sentence structures to make the writing more interesting? ☐ yes ☐ no

Are there any spelling or punctuation mistakes? ☐ yes ☐ no

Are there any grammar errors? ☐ yes ☐ no

Two things I really liked about the writer's story:

1. _____
   _____
   _____

2. _____
   _____
   _____

One thing I think the writer could do to improve the writing:

1. _____
   _____
   _____

Other comments or notes:

Persuasive/Argument Writing Map

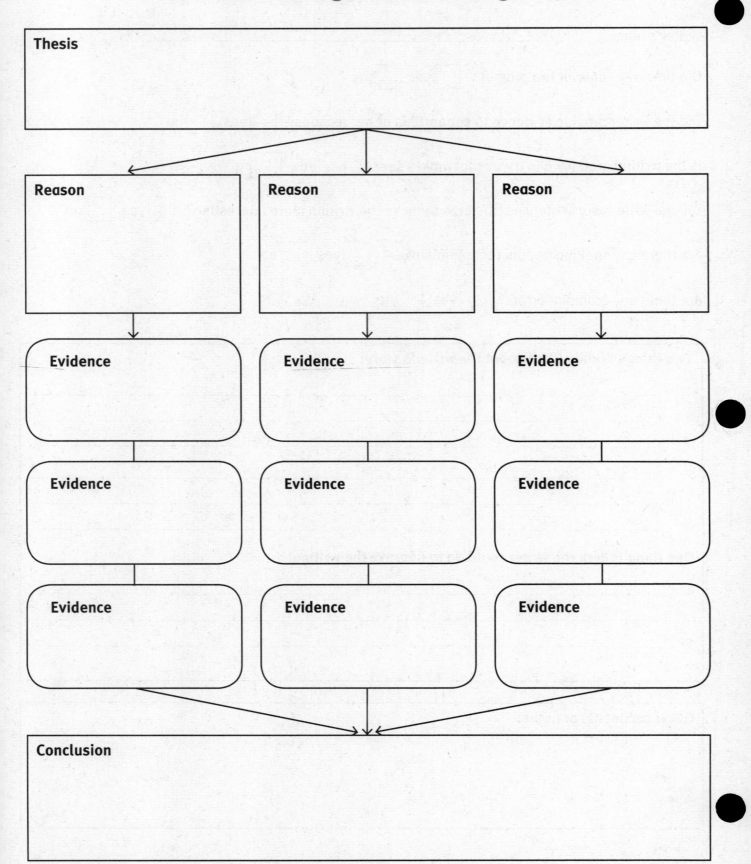

Thesis

| Reason | Reason | Reason |

| Evidence | Evidence | Evidence |

| Evidence | Evidence | Evidence |

| Evidence | Evidence | Evidence |

Conclusion

Roots and Affixes Brainstorm

Directions: Write the root or affix in the circle. Brainstorm or use a dictionary to find the meaning of the root or affix and add it to the circle. Then, find words that use that root or affix. Write one word in each box. Write a sentence for each word.

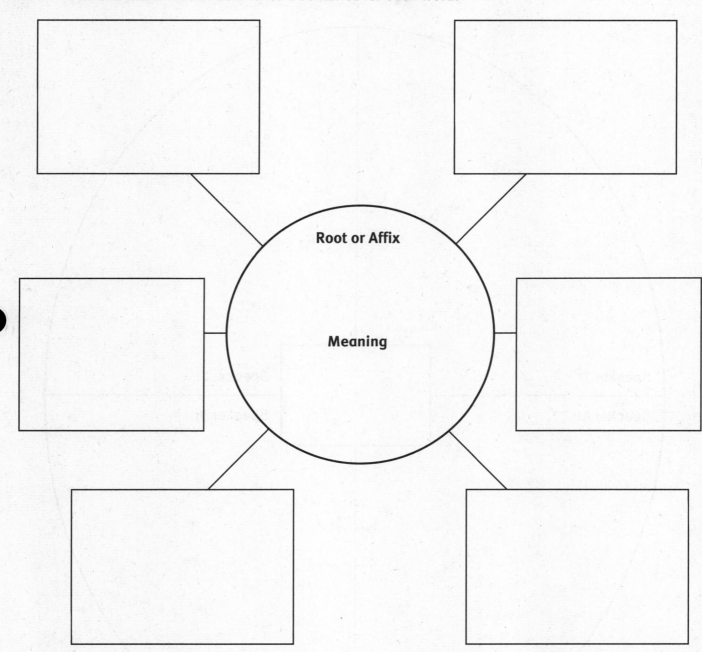

Round Table Discussion

Directions: Write the topic in the center box. One student begins by stating his or her ideas while the student to the left takes notes. Then the next student speaks while the student to his or her left takes notes, and so on.

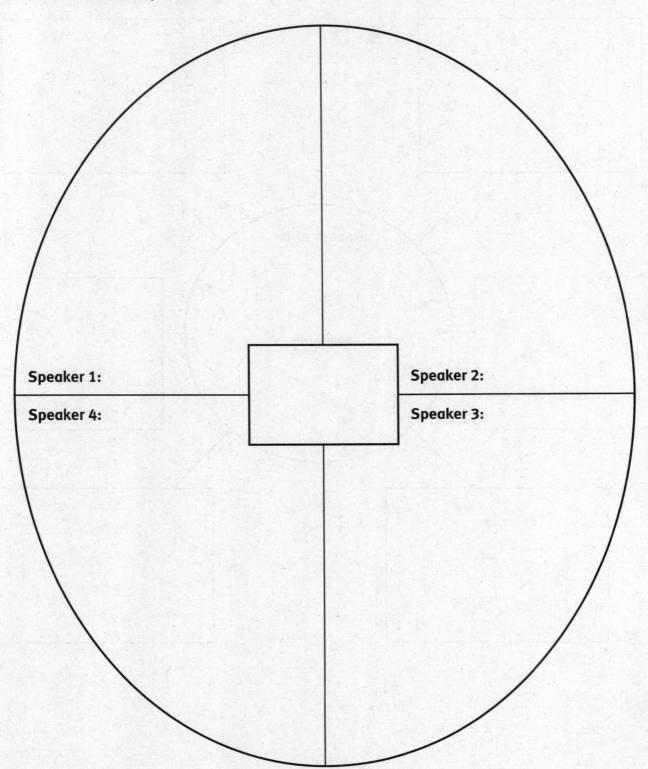

Speaker 1:

Speaker 2:

Speaker 4:

Speaker 3:

Sequence of Events Time Line

Title: _____

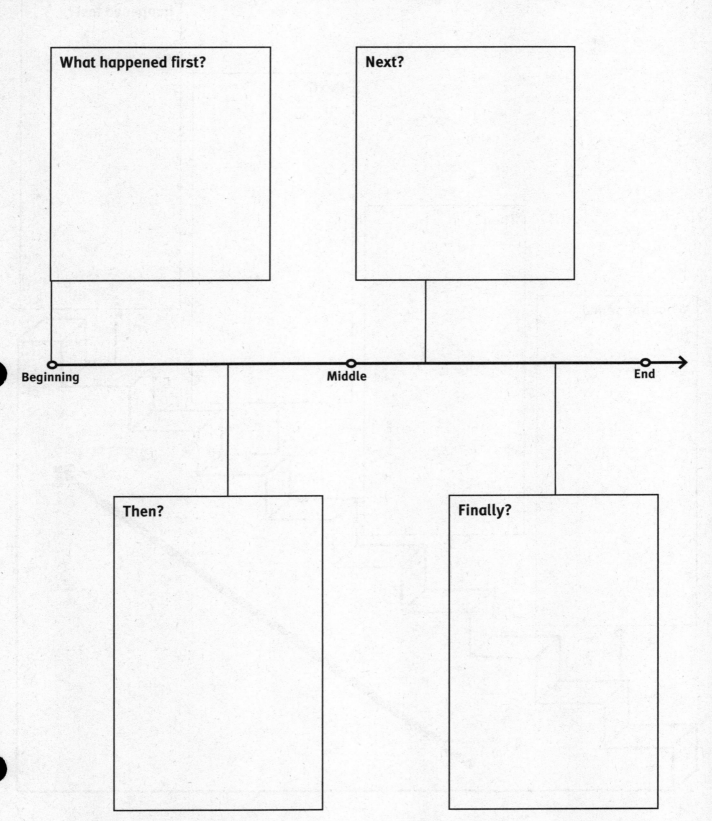

What happened first?

Next?

Beginning   Middle   End

Then?

Finally?

Text Structure Stairs

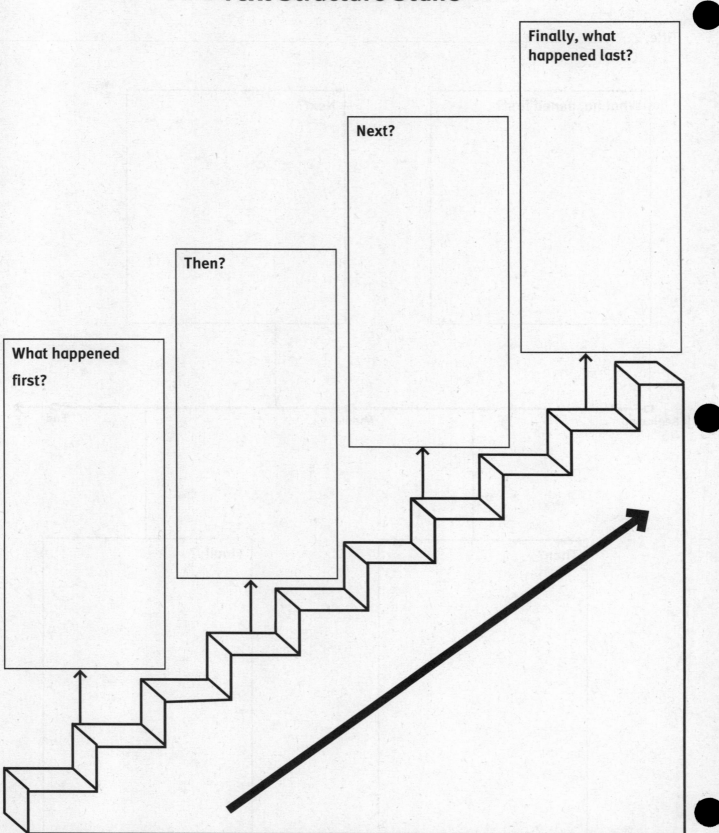

Finally, what happened last?

Next?

Then?

What happened first?

NAME _____ DATE _____   **201**

Unknown Word Solver

Unknown Word

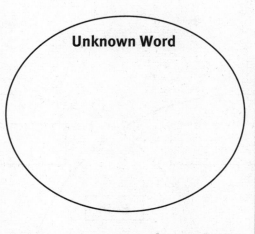

Can you find any context clues? List them.

Do you recognize any word parts?

Prefix:

Root Word:

Suffix:

Do you know another meaning of this word that does not make sense in this context?

Does it look or sound like a word in another language?

What is the dictionary definition?

How can you define the word in your own words?

Venn Diagram for Writing a Comparison

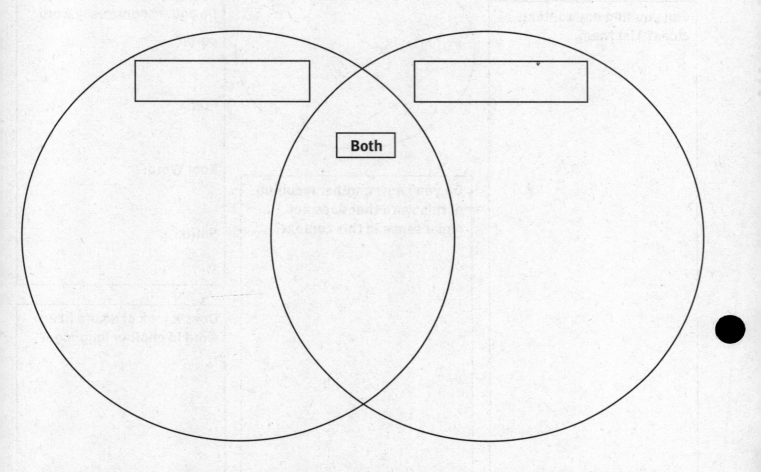

Both

They are similar in that _____
_____
_____
_____
_____
_____
_____

They are different in that _____
_____
_____
_____
_____
_____
_____

Word Choice Analyzer

Word or phrase from the text	What does the word or phrase mean?	What is another way to say the same thing?	What effect did the author produce by choosing these words?

Explain Your Analysis

The author uses the word or phrase _____, which means

_____

Another way to say this is _____

_____

I think the author chose these words to _____

_____

_____

One way I can modify this sentence to add detail is to _____

_____

Phonemes Chart

PHONEMES

Phonemes are sounds. You can remember this by noticing the Greek root *phone-*, which means to *listen*. You have probably noticed this root in the words *telephone* or *microphone*.

Each letter in the alphabet has its own sound, or phoneme. When these phoneme parts are put together, they make up the sound of a word. Knowing phonemes is important because it helps you to decode words quickly as you read. Here are some ideas to help you learn phonemes:

1 Say each phoneme in the chart. Then read aloud the key words. As you say the word, pay special attention to the phonemes that are underlined. For example, for /a/, you might say: *haaaabitaaaat*. Be careful with phonemes blend sounds together, such as: *ouch*. In this example, the /ow/ sound should be focused on, not the /o/ or the /u/ alone.

2 Choose one of the phonemes and then find other words that rhyme: *brew, blew, chew, drew, crew, grew.*

3 Have you heard of tongue twisters? They are sentences that use the same letters over and over. One example is: *Silly Sodhka sells seashells by the sandy sea shore.* Choose one of the phonemes and try to come up with your own tongue twister.

4 Work with a partner or a family member. Take turns saying words. Then try to guess which phoneme the word starts or ends with.

5 Write phonemes on many index cards. Shuffle them and pick a few cards. Put them together to make new words. It's even better if they are not real words! Say the new words aloud.

Category	Phoneme	Common Graphemes	Key Words
Short Vowel Sounds	/a/	a, au	h<u>a</u>bit<u>a</u>t, v<u>au</u>lt
	/e/	e, ea	d<u>e</u>finite, st<u>ea</u>dfast
	/i/	i	h<u>i</u>story, rel<u>i</u>c
	/o/	o, a, au, aw, ough	pl<u>o</u>t, cl<u>au</u>se
	/u/	u, o	<u>u</u>ntil, cl<u>u</u>tter
Long Vowel Sounds	/ā/	a, a_e, ay, ai, ey, ei	dec<u>ay</u>, det<u>ai</u>n, f<u>a</u>ble
	/ē/	e, e_e, ea, ee, ey, ie, y	<u>e</u>quality, refer<u>ee</u>, troll<u>ey</u>
	/ī/	i, i_e, igh, y, ie	emph<u>a</u>size, th<u>igh</u>, th<u>y</u>
	/ō/	o, o_e, oa, ou, ow	th<u>o</u>rough, em<u>o</u>tion, afl<u>oa</u>t
	/ū/	u, u_e, ew	br<u>ew</u>, spect<u>a</u>cular, substit<u>u</u>te
Other Vowel Sounds	/oo/	oo, u, oul	childh<u>oo</u>d, c<u>ou</u>ld, camp<u>u</u>s
	/ōō/	oo, u, u_e	cart<u>oo</u>n, intr<u>u</u>de, br<u>u</u>te
Vowel Diphthongs	/ow/	ow, ou, ou_e	tr<u>ow</u>el, v<u>ou</u>ch, ar<u>ou</u>se
	/oy/	oi, oy	empl<u>oy</u>, rec<u>oi</u>l, b<u>oi</u>ler
R-Controlled Vowels	/a(r)/	ar	bomb<u>ar</u>d, rad<u>ar</u>
	/ā(r)/	air, ear, are	<u>ear</u>shot, aff<u>air</u>, welf<u>are</u>
	/i(r)/	irr, ere, eer	<u>irr</u>egular, m<u>ere</u>, sh<u>eer</u>
	/o(r)/	or, ore, oor	sh<u>or</u>tage, c<u>ore</u>, m<u>oor</u>ing
	/u(r)/	ur, ir, er, ear, or, ar	p<u>ur</u>ify, reh<u>ear</u>sal, cal<u>or</u>ie

Category	Phoneme	Common Graphemes	Key Words
Consonant Sounds	/b/	b, bb	butler, hobble
	/d/	d, dd, ed	meddle, decimal, unexpected
	/f/	f, ph	curfew, phantom
	/g/	g, gg	jagged, peg
	/h/	h	habitation, herd
	/j/	j, g, ge, dge	project, outrage, judge
	/k/	c, k, ck, ch, cc, que	arc, slack, technical, unique
	/l/	l, ll	ballad, ruthless
	/m/	m, mm, mb	recommend, ambassador
	/n/	n, nn, kn, gn	annoy, knead, reign, nun
	/p/	p, pp	appease, policy
	/r/	r, rr, wr	wrath, barren, poetry
	/s/	s, se, ss, c, ce, sc	recede, assault, relapse
	/t/	t, tt, ed	antler, putty
	/v/	v, ve	eaves, pave
	/w/	w	winter, dwell
	/y/	y, i	yacht, union
	/z/	z, zz, ze, s, se, x	xylophone, grizzly, immerse
Consonant Digraphs	/th/ (not voiced)	th	blacksmith, sheath, breadth
	/th/ (voiced)	th	ruthless, athlete, sympathetic
	/ng/	ng, n	boomerang, bankrupt
	/sh/	sh, ss, ch, ti, ci	ashore, caution, assure
	/ch/	ch, tch	research, twitch
	/j/	ge, s	camouflage, version
	/wh/ (with breath)	wh	wheeze, whim, whimper

Glossary/Glosario

A

active voice verb: a verb that expresses an action done by its subject

verbo en voz activa: verbo que expresa una acción realizada por el sujeto

adjectival phrase: a group of words that function as an adjective

frase adjetiva: grupo de palabras que funciona como adjetivo

adjective: a word that modifies a noun or pronoun

adjetivo: palabra que modifica a un sustantivo o pronombre

adverb: a word that describes a verb, an adjective, or another adverb; often shows time, manner, place, or degree

adverbio: palabra que describe a un verbo, adjetivo u otro adverbio y que con frecuencia indica tiempo, modo, lugar o grado

affix: a word part that, when added to the beginning or end of a root or word, changes the word's meaning. A prefix is an affix added to the beginning of a word; a suffix is an affix added to the end of a word.

afijo: parte de una palabra que cambia el significado de la palabra cuando se coloca al principio o al final de la raíz de la palabra. El prefijo es un tipo de afijo que se coloca al principio de la palabra, mientras que el sufijo es un tipo de afijo que se coloca al final de la palabra.

analyze: to study or look at something carefully and closely

analizar: estudiar u observar algo cuidadosamente y de cerca

antonyms: words that mean the opposite of each other

antónimos: palabras con significados opuestos

appositive: a noun or pronoun placed besides another noun or pronoun to identify or explain it

aposición: sustantivo o pronombre colocado junto a otro sustantivo o pronombre para identificarlo o describirlo

appositive phrase: an appositive and its modifiers; appositives and appositive phrases are usually set off with commas

frase apositiva: una aposición y sus modificadores; las aposiciones y frases apositivas generalmente van entre comas

argument: a set of reasons given to persuade others that an idea or action is right or wrong; an argument is stronger if it supported by evidence

argumento: conjunto de razones usado para persuadir a otros de que cierta idea o acción es correcta o incorrecta; los argumentos más solidos usan evidencia como apoyo

audience: the people who will read a text, listen to a speech, or view a performance

público: las personas que leerán un texto, escucharán un discurso o acudirán a una presentación

author's purpose: the reason that the author is writing a work: to inform, to entertain, or to persuade

propósito del autor: la razón por la cual el autor escribe una obra, como informar, entretener o persuadir

B

base word: a word with no prefix or suffix

base de la palabra: palabra sin prefijo o sufijo

C

central idea: the theme or most important message in a literary work

idea central: el tema o mensaje más importante en una obra literaria

character: a person, animal, or imaginary being that takes part in the action of a story

personaje: persona, animal o ser imaginario que forma parte de la acción de un cuento

characterization: the way an author develops a story's characters, by describing their appearance, actions, words, and thoughts

caracterización: métodos que usa un autor para desarrollar los personajes de un cuento al describir su apariencia, acciones, palabras y pensamientos

citation: a quote of or reference to a source of evidence

cita: referencia a una fuente de información o evidencia

claim: an assertion of something as true, real, or factual; to say something is true

declaración: aseveración de que algo es cierto, real o fáctico

climax: the peak of the action; the most intense or suspenseful moment, often a turning point in the story

clímax: la cima de la acción; el momento más intenso o intrigante que, por lo general, cambia el curso de una historia

cognates: words in different languages that are formed from the same original word or root

cognados: palabras que comparten la misma raíz en diferentes idiomas

commentary: a discussion in which people write or share orally their opinion about someone or something

comentario: conversación en la cual personas escriben o comparten sus opiniones de manera oral

compare: to show how two or more things are alike or similar

comparar: identificar semejanzas en dos o más elementos

complex sentence: a sentence that has an independent clause and one or more dependent clauses

oración compleja subordinada: una oración que contiene una cláusula independiente y una o varias cláusulas dependientes

compound sentence: a sentence with two independent clauses joined by a semicolon or comma and a coordinating conjunction such as and, or, but, not, or so
oración compuesta: oración con dos cláusulas independientes unidas por un punto y coma o coma y por una conjunción coordinante, como lo son y, pero, no, así que

compound-complex sentence: a sentence made from two independent clauses and one or more dependent clauses
oración compuesta con cláusulas subordinadas: oración formada por dos cláusulas independientes y una o más cláusulas dependientes o subordinadas

conclusion: the ending of a paragraph, essay, or story, which brings it to a close and leaves an impression with the reader
conclusión: fin de un párrafo, ensayo o cuento corto que lo lleva a su término y que deja una impresión en el lector

context clue: information in words and phrases surrounding an unfamiliar word that hint at the meaning of the unfamiliar word
clave de contexto: información en las palabras y frases que rodean una palabra no conocida y que dan una pista acerca del significado de esa palabra

contrast: to show how two or more things are different or opposite
contrastar: identificar las diferencias entre dos o más elementos

convey: to make known or understood
transmitir: expresar algo para darlo a conocer

D

dependent clause: a group of words that include a subject and a verb but do not express a complete thought and cannot stand alone as a sentence
cláusula subordinada: grupo de palabras con sujeto y verbo pero que no expresa un pensamiento completo y que no funciona como oración completa

description: the type of writing or speech that creates a colorful, exact picture of a person, place, object, or event
descripción: tipo de escrito o discurso que genera una imagen precisa y colorida de una persona, lugar, objeto o suceso

dialogue: the words spoken by a character in a story, film, or play; in written texts, dialogue is set inside quotation marks
diálogo: las palabras que forman el diálogo de un personaje en un cuento, película u obra de teatro; en los escritos, el diálogo va ente comillas

drama: a play that tells a story and is performed
obra de teatro: escrito que relata una historia y que es puesto en escena

E

editorial: a short essay in a publication in which someone expresses an opinion on an issue
editorial/artículo de opinión: ensayo corto en una publicación donde alguien expresa su opinión sobre un tema

effective: producing an effect or result
eficaz: que produce un efecto o resultado

evaluate: to judge or determine the significance, worth, or quality of something
evaluar: juzgar o determinar la importancia, el valor o la calidad de algo

evidence: the facts, details, and information that support the reasons for a claim
evidencia: los hechos, detalles e información que apoyan el razonamiento en una declaración

explanation: writing or speech that makes something easy to understand
explicación: escrito o discurso que hace que algo sea fácil de entender

exposition: the part of a story that introduces background information about the characters and setting
exposición: parte de un cuento que presenta información de fondo sobre los personajes y el ambiente

expository writing: writing that delivers information and usually includes a main idea with supporting details
texto expositivo: escrito que proporciona información y que por lo general incluye una idea principal y detalles de apoyo

external conflict: a conflict in which the character struggles with an outside force, such as another person or something in nature
conflicto externo: conflicto en donde el personaje lucha con una fuerza externa, como alguna otra persona o algún elemento de la naturaleza

F

fact: information that is true, that can be proven
hecho: información que es cierta, que puede demostrarse

falling action: the events that lead to the ending of a story
acción descendente: sucesos que dan pie al final o la resolución de un cuento

fiction: a story about a person or event that is not true or is imagined
ficción: cuento sobre una persona que no es real o sobre un suceso imaginario

figurative language: imaginative language that is not meant to be interpreted literally, but to create an effect on the reader
lenguaje figurativo: lenguaje imaginativo que no pretende ser interpretado literalmente, sino crear un efecto en el lector

first person point of view: the storytelling perspective in which the narrator is a character in the story telling what he or she sees or knows
punto de vista de primera persona: perspectiva para contar cuentos en la cual el narrador es un personaje en el cuento y que cuenta lo que ve o lo que piensa

formal style: a style of writing or speaking that is appropriate for formal communication such as in academics or business
estilo formal: tipo de escrito o discurso apropiado para situaciones de comunicación formal, como lo son el ámbito académico y el de negocios

format: the kind of writing the author has produced such as a story or poem; the way a text is organized
formato: modo de organizar un escrito, como un cuento o poema

free verse: a kind of poetry that uses no rhyme
verso libre: tipo de poesía que no rima

H

hook: a sentence or phrase that writers use to grab the reader's attention
gancho: idea o frase que los autores usan para captar la atención del lector

I

iambic pentameter: A rhythm in a line of poetry that has 10 unstressed/stressed beats per line
pentámetro yámbico: el ritmo en un verso que lleva 10 sílabas en total, cinco acentuadas y cinco no acentuadas

identify: to recognize or find
identificar: reconocer o encontrar

imagery: the use of words to create mental pictures; word pictures created by descriptive, sensory, or figurative language
imaginería: el uso de palabras para crear imágenes mentales; la imaginería es creada a través de lenguaje descriptivo, sensorial o figurativo

incident: the central piece of action that is the focus of the narrative
incidente: parte central de la acción en que se enfoca la narrativa

independent clause: a group of words that expresses a complete thought and can stand by itself as a simple sentence
cláusula independiente: grupo de palabras que expresa un pensamiento completo y que puede funcionar como oración simple

inference: a logical conclusion or guess based on textual evidence, prior experience, or observation

inferencia: conjetura o conclusión lógica basada en la observación, experiencias anteriores o evidencia textual

inflection: the rise or fall of a person's voice while speaking
inflexión: énfasis que pone un orador en las palabras al cambiar de tono o volumen

internal conflict: when a character is torn by two feelings, decisions, or values
conflicto interno: cuando un personaje está divido entre dos sentimientos, decisiones o valores

introduction: the opening or beginning of a story or other written work that presents the central idea or argument in a thesis statement
introducción: párrafo inicial de un cuento o texto que presenta la idea central o el argumento de una tesis

irregular verb: a verb that forms its past and past participle in some way other than by adding –d or –ed to the base form
verbo irregular: en inglés, verbo cuya conjugación en tiempo pretérito y cuyo participio no se forman al añadir –d o –ed después de la base o raíz de la palabra

issue: an important subject or topic that people are talking or thinking about
asunto: tema importante del que hablan o en el que piensan las personas

L

logos: a rhetorical appeal that uses logical reasoning and evidence
logos: apelación retórica que usa razonamiento lógico y evidencia

M

metaphor: a kind of figurative language in which something is described by comparing it to something else
metáfora: tipo de lenguaje figurativo que describe una cosa al compararla con otra

morphology: the study of the forms of words
morfología: el estudio de las formas de las palabras

multiple-meaning word: a word that has more than one meaning or can be used as more than one part of speech
palabra con múltiples significados: palabra que tiene más de un significado o que puede funcionar como varias categorías gramaticales

N

narrative: writing that tells a story or describes a sequence of events in an incident
narrativa: tipo de escrito que cuenta un cuento o que describe una secuencia de sucesos

narrator: the character or person telling a story or poem
narrador: el personaje o persona que relata un cuento o poema

nonfiction: a story or writing that is based on facts or something that really happened
no ficción: cuento o escrito basado en hechos o acontecimientos reales

noun phrase: a noun and its modifiers
frase subjuntiva: frase compuesta por un sustantivo y sus modificadores

novel: a work of literature that tells a long fictional story
novela: tipo de género literario que cuenta una historia ficticia larga

O

object: a person or thing that receives the action and is often preceded by a verb
complemento: persona o cosa que recibe la acción del verbo y que con frecuencia precede al verbo

opinion: a belief or idea that can be debated
opinión: perspectiva o creencia debatible

oral interpretation: reading aloud literature while expressing meaning of the words
interpretación oral: leer un texto literario en voz alta de manera que comunique los significados de las palabras

P

paraphrase: to restate something in your own words
parafrasear: reformular algo usando tus propias palabras

passive voice: narrative voice that emphasizes the person or thing receiving the action rather than the one performing the action
voz pasiva: voz narrativa que pone énfasis en la persona o cosa que recibe la acción en lugar de aquellas que realizan la acción

passive voice verb: a verb that expresses an action done to its subject
verbo en voz pasiva: verbo que expresa la acción que afecta al sustantivo

pathos: a rhetorical appeal to the reader's or listener's feelings
pathos: apelación retórica a los sentidos o emociones del lector u oyente

personal narrative: a story based on one's own life and told in the first person point of view; describes an incident, and includes a response and a reflection on the incident
narrativa personal: cuento con base en la vida propia, relatado en primera persona, que describe un acontecimiento y que incluye una reflexión acerca del acontecimiento

personification: the act of giving human qualities to non-human things
personificación: tipo de metáfora que da o atribuye características humanas a objetos o seres no humanos

persuasion: the act or skill of causing someone to do or believe something
persuasión: acto o destreza de poder hacer que alguien haga o crea algo

point of view: the perspective from which a story is told
punto de vista: perspectiva desde la cual se cuenta una historia

precise: exact, specific
preciso: exacto, específico

preposition: a word that shows the relationship of a noun or pronoun to some other word in the sentence
preposición: palabra que muestra la relación entre un sustantivo o pronombre y alguna otra palabra en la oración

prepositional phrase: a group of words that includes preposition, a noun or pronoun called the object of a preposition, and any modifiers of the preposition
frase preposicional: grupo de palabras que consiste de una preposición, un sustantivo o pronombre que funciona como complemento de dicha preposición y cualquier otro modificador preposicional

pronoun: a part of speech that takes the place of a noun, or refers back to a noun
pronombre: categoría gramátical que toma el lugar de un sustantivo o que hace referencia a algún sustantivo ya pasado

R

reason: an explanation of one's thinking, belief, or opinion
razón: explicación sobre los pensamientos, creencias u opiniones de una persona

reflection: thinking and writing that seriously explores the significance of an experience, idea, or observation
reflexión: tipo de pensamiento y escritura que explora seriamente la importancia de una experiencia, idea u observación

regular verb: a verb that forms its past and past participle by adding –d or –ed to its base form
verbo regular: en inglés, verbo cuyo pasado y pasado participio consiste en agregar una –d o –ed después de la base de la palabra

repetition: the repeated use of the same words or phrases for effect
repetición: repetición de las mismas palabras o frases para crear efecto

research: to locate reliable information from a variety of sources; the noun research also describes the information found from the search
investigar: (v.) proceso de buscar información en una variedad de fuentes; también, investigación (n.) información que se halla al investigar una variedad de fuentes

resolution: the point at the end of the story when the conflict is resolved and the theme is revealed; the conclusion
resolución: la parte final de un cuento en donde se resuelve el conflicto y se revela el tema; la conclusión

response: the immediate emotions and actions associated with the incident in a story
reacción: las emociones y acciones inmediatas asociadas con el acontecimiento o incidente de un cuento

revision: a process of evaluating writing to improve language and coherence
revisión: proceso de evaluar un texto escrito para mejorar la coherencia y el uso del lenguaje

rewrite: to write again or revise to make something different
reescribir: volver a escribir o revisar un texto para cambiar algo

rhetorical appeals: persuasive strategies used in arguments to support claim
apelaciones retóricas: estrategias de persuasión que sirven para apoyar una declaración

rhyme scheme: a consistent pattern of end rhyme throughout a poem
esquema de la rima: patrón consistente de una rima final a lo largo de un poema

rhythm: the pattern of stressed and unstressed syllables in a poem
ritmo de un poema: patrón de sílabas acentuadas y no acentuadas en un poema

rising action: the main events that form the plot of a story; these events lead to the story's climax
acción ascendente: sucesos importantes que desarrollan la trama de un cuento y conducen al clímax

role: how the author is connected to the story
rol: posición que toma el autor en un cuento

root word: a word or word part that is the basis for other words
raíz de la palabra: una palabra o parte de una palabra que constituye la base de otras palabras

S

sensory language: words and details that are used to appeal to a reader's five senses: sight, hearing, touch, smell, and taste.
lenguaje sensorial: palabras y detalles que apelan a los cinco sentidos del lector: vista, oído, tacto, olfato y gusto

setting: the time and place in which a story takes place
ambiente: tiempo y lugar en que ocurre un relato

short story: a short work of fiction; plot structure includes rising action, climax, falling action, and resolution
cuento corto: obra de ficción que es corta y cuya estructura presenta una trama con acción ascendente, clímax, acción descendente y resolución

simile: a kind of figurative language in which a phrase describes something by comparing it to something else, using the words "like" or "as"
símil: tipo de lenguaje figurativo que hace descripciones usando frases para comparar dos cosas usando las palabras "como" o "tan"

simple sentence: a sentence with one independent clause (contains a subject and verb)
oración simple: oración con una sola cláusula independiente que lleva un sujeto y un verbo

source: a person, book, publication, or Website that gives information about a topic
fuente: persona, libro, publicación o sitio en línea que proporciona información sobre un tema

structure: how a text is organized
estructura: la organización de un texto

style: how an author uses words and phrases to form his or her ideas
estilo: la manera en que el autor usa palabras y frases para formar sus ideas

subject: a person or thing that performs an action and is often followed by a verb; the person, idea, or topic that a piece of writing is about
sujeto: persona u objeto que realiza una acción y que con frecuencia precede al verbo; la persona, idea o tópico sobre el cual trata un escrito

subordinating conjunctions: specific words that connect an adverbial clause to the word or words the clause modifies or describes—although, because, that, when, while, whenever, as long as
conjunciones subordinadas: palabras específicas que conectan una cláusula adverbial con la palabra o las palabras que son modificadas o descritas por dicha cláusula

suffix: a word part added to the ending of a base word to change the word's meaning
sufijo: parte de una palabra que cambia el significado de la palabra cuando se coloca al final de la raíz de la palabra

summarize: to briefly restate the main ideas of a piece of writing
resumir: replantear de manera breve las ideas principales de un escrito

summary: a short restatement of the main points of a text
resumen: una declaración breve sobre los puntos principales de un texto

supporting details: facts or information that tell about a topic; they support the main idea
detalles de apoyo: hechos o información que dicen algo sobre un tópico y que apoyan la idea principal

synonym: a word that has the same or a very similar definition as another word
sinónimos: palabras con significados iguales o semejantes

synthesize: to combine different things or ideas into a new idea

sintetizar: combinar cosas diferentes o ideas para producir una idea nueva

T

technique: a method used by an author to provide readers with a deeper understanding

técnica: método usado por un autor para facilitar la comprensión profunda del lector

textual evidence: facts, details, quotations, summaries, or paraphrases from text passages to support a position

evidencia textual: hechos, detalles, citas, resúmenes o paráfrasis de pasajes de texto que apoyan una postura

theme: the central message or insight about life that a piece of literature portrays through its characters, plot, imagery, and other details

tema: el mensaje central o percepción sobre la vida que una obra literaria representa a través de los personajes, la trama, la imaginería y otros detalles

thesis statement: the central idea or claim being made in a written work about a topic

enunciado de tesis: la idea central o declaración de un escrito sobre un tópico

third person point of view: the storytelling perspective in which the narrator is someone outside the story

punto de vista de tercera persona: perspectiva para contar cuentos en donde el narrador es alguien afuera del contexto del cuento

tone: the attitude that a writer or speaker displays toward his or her subject

tono: actitud de un escritor u orador hacia un tema

topic: the subject of what the author has written about

tópico: el tema sobre el cual el autor ha escrito

topic sentence: a sentence that expresses the key thought or idea of a paragraph or written piece of work

oración principal: oración que plantea la idea principal de un párrafo o escrito

trait: a quality or characteristic that makes a character unique or different

rasgo: atributo o característica que hace que un personaje sea único o diferente

transition words: words or phrases that connect ideas, details, or events in writing

palabras de transición: palabras o frases que conectan ideas, detalles o sucesos de un escrito

V

verb: a word that expresses action or a state of being

verbo: palabra que expresa acción o estado anímico

vivid verbs: specific verbs that describe action in clear detail and add excitement

verbos vívidos: verbos específicos que describen una acción a detalle y que añaden emoción

Index

Academic collaboration, 8, 21, 34, 53, 66, 77, 95, 108, 120, 140, 152, 165
Academic language/vocabulary, 2, 3, 15, 16, 28, 29, 49, 60, 61, 73, 74, 90, 91, 103, 115, 116, 134, 135, 147, 148, 160
Academic Vocabulary, 11, 56, 69, 80, 98, 143, 155, 168
Active listening, 8, 21, 34, 43, 53, 86, 88, 95, 108, 129, 173
Active voice verbs, 123
Adjectival phrases, 54
Adjectives, 54
    Possessive, 9
Adverbials, 98
Adverb phrases, 98
Adverbs, 98, 100
    Modal, 11
Affixes, 15, 73, 159, 168
Agreeing, sentence starters for, 101
Analyze language
    Figurative language, 35, 36
    Sensory language, 155
Analyze literature
    Autobiography, 73
    Compare and contrast, 56
    Drama, 159
    Editorial, 90
    Informational text, 134
    Letter, 115
    Memoir, 60
    News article, 102
    Novel, 48
    Personal narrative, 2
    Plot, 37
    Poem, 147
    Short story, 15, 28
Annotating text, 5, 18, 31, 51, 63, 67, 76, 93, 105, 118, 137, 145, 150, 162
Answering questions, 8, 34, 53, 66, 88, 95, 108, 120, 140, 152, 165
Antonyms, 50, 104
Appositive phrase, 111
Appositives, 111
Argument
    Rhetorical appeals, 115
        logos, 115
        pathos, 115
    In speaking, 90, 100, 101, 111
    In writing, 12, 23, 55, 57, 70, 81, 99, 100, 111, 112, 113, 124
Argumentative letter, 125
Asking questions, 8, 21, 34, 53, 66, 88, 95, 108, 120, 140, 152, 165
Attitude, 67
Audience, 27, 71, 123

Author's purpose, 60, 71
Autobiography, 73, 76
Background knowledge, 13
Brainstorming
    Oral presentation, 170
    Writing, 39, 82, 125
Cause/effect
    In reading, 145
    Transition words for, 80
Character, 2, 5, 48
    In dramatic presentation, 170
    In literature, 5, 21
        details, 56
        main character, 21
        similarities and differences, 58
    In writing, 39, 41
Characterization, 28, 48
    In literature, 48, 54
        actions, 48, 58
        appearance, 58
        description, 48
        dialogue, 48
        traits, 48, 55
        words, 58
    In writing
        actions, 39
        feelings, 39
Claim, 90, 93, 100, 101, 108, 113, 114, 120, 125
Claim-reason-evidence structure, 114, 125
Claim-reason-supporting details, 101
Clauses
    Combining, 56, 58, 80, 143, 145
    Dependent, 78, 143
    Embedded, 98
    Independent, 78, 143
    Subordinate, 141
Climax, 15, 24, 34, 37, 38
Close reading, 5, 18, 31, 51, 58, 63, 76, 93, 95, 105, 108, 118, 120, 137, 145, 150
Cognates, 2, 60, 134, 147
Collaborative conversations, 8, 21, 34, 53, 66, 95, 108, 120, 140, 152, 165
Collaborative writing, 58, 69, 71, 113, 157
Commentary, 48
Compare, 38, 56
Compare and contrast, 26
    In reading, 145
    In speaking, 25, 27
    Transitions, 56
    In writing, 26
Complex sentences, 78, 143
Compound-complex sentences, 143

Compound sentences, 56, 58, 143, 145
Comprehension, 5, 16, 18, 24, 31, 37, 56, 135, 143
Conclusion (ending), 73, 84
Conclusions, drawing, 58, 76, 95, 105, 108, 120, 137, 140, 145, 150, 162
Conflict, 21, 22, 23, 37, 38
    External, 15, 37
    Internal, 15, 37
    In writing, 39, 41
Conjunctions, subordinate, 141, 142
Context clues, 93, 137, 166, 168
Contrast, 56. *See also* Compare and contrast
Debate, 100
    Negotiate, 100
    Persuade, 100
Dependent clause, 78, 143
Details, 39, 42, 98
    Of characters, 56
    With noun phrases, 111, 155
    Supporting, 60, 90, 100, 101
Dialogue
    In literature, 26, 28
    In speaking, 142
    In writing, 41
Diction (word choice), 2, 22, 27
    Academic language, 2, 3, 15, 16, 28, 29, 49, 60, 61, 73, 74, 90, 91, 103, 115, 116, 134, 135, 147, 148, 160
    Social language/vocabulary, 3, 16, 29, 49, 61, 74, 91, 103, 116, 123, 135, 148, 160
Disagreeing, sentence starters for, 101
Discussion notes, 84
Drafting, 41, 85, 127
Drama, 159, 162, 170
Dramatic presentation, 170
Drawing conclusions, 58, 76, 95, 105, 108, 120, 137, 140, 145, 150, 162
Editing, 42, 85, 127
    Peer Editing Checklist, 42, 85, 127
Editorial, 90, 93, 100
Effect, 23
    In literature, 11, 22, 23, 35, 67, 80
    In writing, 23, 121, 143
Embedded assessment, 40–42, 82–86, 125–129, 170–173
Essay
    Explanatory, 144
    Expository, 82
Evaluate, 80
Evidence, 100, 111, 113, 114, 125, 155. *See also* Textual evidence
Explanation, 25

Index of Authors and Titles

Credits